TEXAS
INSTRUMENTS

z=.881   p=.3783

STATISTICS HANDBOOK FOR THE TI-83

Larry Morgan,
Montgomery County Community College,
Blue Bell, PA

Important notice regarding book materials

Texas Instruments makes no warranty, either expressed or implied, including but not limited to any implied warranties of merchantability and fitness for a particular purpose, regarding any programs or book materials and makes such materials available solely on an "as-is" basis. In no event shall Texas Instruments be liable to anyone for special, collateral, incidental, or consequential damages in connection with or arising out of the purchase or use of these materials, and the sole and exclusive liability of Texas Instruments, regardless of the form of action, shall not exceed the purchase price of this book. Moreover, Texas Instruments shall not be liable for any claim of any kind whatsoever against the use of these materials by any other party.

Permission is hereby granted to teachers to reprint or photocopy in classroom, workshop, or seminar quantities the pages or sheets in this work that carry a Texas Instruments copyright notice. These pages are designed to be reproduced by teachers for use in their classes, workshops, or seminars, provided each copy made shows the copyright notice. Such copies may not be sold and further distribution is expressly prohibited. Except as authorized above, prior written permission must be obtained from Texas Instruments Incorporated to reproduce or transmit this work or portions thereof in any other form or by any other electronic or mechanical means, including any information storage or retrieval system, unless expressly permitted by federal copyright law. Address inquiries to Texas Instruments Incorporated, 7800 Banner Drive, M/S 3918, Dallas, TX 75251, Attention: Manager, Business Services.

We invite your feedback on the material in this book. Call us at **1-800-TI-CARES,** or send us e-mail at **ticares@ti.com** with your suggestions or comments. You may also call or send e-mail to obtain information about other current and future publications from Texas Instruments.

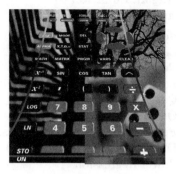

CONTENTS

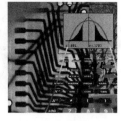

Preface

The *Statistics Handbook for the TI-83* is intended as an aid in using the TI-83 graphing calculator with most introductory statistics texts. The TI-83's powerful statistical features allow you to concentrate on important ideas and concepts rather than on mechanical computations. This handbook demonstrates, with examples, how to use the features of the TI-83 to solve problems or to clarify ideas and concepts from your text. Your text will explain the appropriateness of the statistical features used and any restrictions.

This handbook consists of beginning instructions and 59 topics. A knowledge of the Introduction and Topic 1 is assumed for the other topics. Topics are grouped under 13 activities—activities *not* chapters—so there will be no confusion with the chapters of your statistics text. Each activity has a brief introduction that covers the topics within that activity. For example, Activity 1 describes one-variable data using data sets of building heights in Philadelphia and other cities. This data is used in the topics in Activity 1 to construct histograms, stem-and-leaf plots, and box plots, and to calculate measures of center, variability, and position.

Fifty-five of the 59 topics use the built-in features of the TI-83. Three advanced topics (multiple regression, two-way analysis of variance (ANOVA), and a time series decomposition) use programs that are available from your instructor or from TI over the internet (www.ti.com) or on disk (1-800-TI-CARES). For ease of reference, these programs are also listed in Appendix B of this handbook. You can transfer the programs to your TI-83 with the TI-GRAPH LINK™. (Information on how to obtain TI-GRAPH LINK is available from 1-800-TI-CARES.)

Most of the topics present a procedure that you can use to work problems from your text. In addition, the following topics present simulations to help clarify important ideas:

Topic 21—The Law of Large Numbers
Topic 25—Distribution of Sample Proportions
Topic 26—Distribution of Sample Means (Central Limit Theorem)
Topic 28—Distribution of the Difference of Two Independent Sample Means
Topic 39—Unbiased and Biased Estimators

Other topics present both a procedure you can use to work problems from your text and also a simulation to clarify the meaning of the results of that procedure. For example, Topic 33 shows how to calculate a confidence interval with the TI-83 and then uses a simulation to explain the meaning of the term "confidence interval."

The outside back cover provides a quick reference to the functions of the TI-83 and the topics within the handbook. Appendix A cross-references two introductory statistics textbooks, providing examples of how the sections of introductory statistics texts can be aided by the topics in this handbook. You can prepare a similar sheet for your text and tape it to the inside back cover of this handbook for a convenient reference.

Finally, a word of thanks to my students and colleagues who have been supportive of using calculators in the classroom. Thanks to Mike Koehler, Blue Valley North High School, and to Walter Walker, Eckerd College, who reviewed the first draft of this handbook and made helpful comments and suggestions. Thanks to Charlotte Andreini, Jeanie Anirudhan, Brenda Curry, Nelah McComsey, and all others at Texas Instruments who helped make this handbook possible. Special thanks to Narissa for her help and to Abui for her continued support.

—*Larry Morgan*

EXPLORATIONS

Do This
First

These instructions give a brief overview of how to use the TI-83 and how to set it up for the topics in this book. Keystroke notations and procedural assumptions are discussed, as well as how to enter data into lists that will be used later in the book.

Adjusting the Display Contrast and Replacing Batteries

You can adjust the display contrast to suit your viewing angle and lighting conditions. As you change the contrast setting, a number from **0** (lightest) to **9** (darkest) in the top-right corner indicates the current level. You may not be able to see the number if contrast is too light or too dark.

Note: The TI-83 has 40 contrast settings, so each number, **0** through **9**, represents four settings.

The TI-83 retains the contrast setting in memory when it is turned off. To adjust the contrast, follow these steps.

1. Press and release the 2nd key.

2. Press and hold ⊡ or ⊡, which are below and above the contrast symbol (yellow, half-shaded circle).
    ⊡ lightens the screen.
    ⊡ darkens the screen.

Note: If you adjust the contrast setting to **0**, the display may become completely blank. To restore the screen, press and release 2nd, and then press and hold ⊡ until the display reappears.

When the batteries are low, a low-battery message is displayed when you turn on the calculator. You need to replace the four AAA batteries soon. (The display contrast may appear very dark after you change batteries. Press and release the 2nd key, and then hold down ⊡ to lighten the display.) Refer to the *TI-83 Guidebook* for more information about replacing the batteries.

Do This First (cont.)

Understanding the TI-83 Keyboard and Setup Used in this Handbook

Setting Modes

In looking at the TI-83 keyboard, note that the MODE key is next to the 2nd key. Press MODE for displays like those shown in screen 1.

Some topics require that the mode be set for two decimal places, as shown in the second line of screen 1. If this is not the case and other values are highlighted, move the cursor to the leftmost choice in any nonconforming row, and press ENTER.

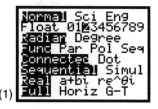

(1)

📖 *For most topics in this handbook, it will be assumed that each mode setting is the leftmost position.*

Using 2nd [QUIT] to Return to the Home Screen

The home screen is the primary screen for entering instructions to execute and expressions to evaluate. It is the screen that displays when you turn on your TI-83. Pressing 2nd [QUIT] (above the MODE key) returns you to the home screen.

Using the CLEAR Key

Start each topic procedure by pressing CLEAR. This clears any line to the left of the cursor or the page above the cursor if there is nothing to its left.

Using Function Plots and Stat Plots

The first row of the keyboard is for setting up and displaying plots and graphs. Press Y= to display screen 2.

📖 *For each topic, it will be assumed that all function plots have been cleared with the CLEAR key or have been deselected.*

The stat plot indicators along the top of the display (**Plot1, Plot2, Plot3**) should not be highlighted. If any of these three plot indicators are highlighted, indicating a stat plot is on, move the cursor to that indicator, and press ENTER to eliminate the highlighting and thus turn off the plot.

```
Plot1 Plot2 Plot3
\Y1=
\Y2=
\Y3=
\Y4=
\Y5=
\Y6=
\Y7=
```

(2)

You can also turn off these plots as follows.

1. Press [2nd] [STAT PLOT] (above the [Y=] key).

    A screen is displayed similar to screen 3, except some of the off indicators are set to on.

2. Select **4** to display **PlotsOff** on the home screen, as shown in the first line in screen 4.

3. Press [ENTER] for **Done** (second line in screen 4), which indicates that all the stat plots are now off.

📖 *For each topic in this handbook, the screen should display as shown in screen 5 when you press [2nd] [FORMAT] (above the [ZOOM] key).*

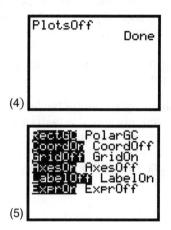

(3)

(4)

(5)

Warning
If any of your setups are different than those described above, your screen displays may not be like the ones shown in this handbook.

Using the [ALPHA] and [STO▸] Keys

Continuing your tour of the keyboard, notice that when you press the green [ALPHA] key, the flashing cursor changes to a flashing **A**. If you press another key at this point, the green letter or symbol above that key is displayed.

Letters may be used for storage. The [STO▸] key is used for storing. It displays an arrow ➔ when pressed (see the display in screen 6 with values stored in **D** and **E**).

Using Basic Operations ([+] [÷] [×] [−] [(-)])

The common mathematical operation keys [÷] and [×] are displayed as **/** and **∗**. Also be aware of the difference between the display of the [−] key (subtraction) symbol and the [(-)] key (negative) symbol. The negative symbol (-) displays shorter and higher than the subtraction symbol (-). (See screen 6 for examples.)

```
-6/2→D
             -3
6-2→E
              4
E∗D
            -12
```

(6)

Do This First (cont.)

Using [2nd] [EE] (-E99, E99)

Note the difference between pressing [2nd] [EE] (above the [,] key) that shows a small capital **E** on the screen and pressing [ALPHA] [E] (above the [SIN] key). Note that **E3** = 10^3 = 1000 while **E3** = **E** $* 3$ = 12, as shown in screen 7, when the value of **E** = 4 as stored in screen 6.

📖 *In this handbook, it will be convenient to use -ε99 as a very large negative number and ε99 as a very large positive number.*

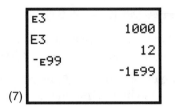

(7)

Using the Advanced Function Keys ([MATH], [MATRX], [PRGM], [2nd] [DISTR])

Continuing your tour of the keyboard, notice the row of advanced function keys [MATH], [MATRX], [PRGM], and [2nd] [DISTR]. You will use them later. The keys [,], [(], and [)], the set or list symbol keys [2nd] [{] and [2nd][}], along with the most important keys [STAT] and [2nd] [LIST] lead us to the next section.

Entering Data into a List From the Home Screen

From the home screen, use the following procedure to store data to a list.

1. Enter the data as shown on the first line of screen 8, with commas between each of the integers from 1 to 5. Do not forget to press [STO▸]. Note that six convenient list names **L1** to **L6** are above the number keys [1] to [6] in yellow so you must first press [2nd] (for example, [2nd] [L1]).

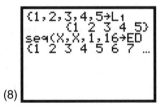

(8)

2. Press [ENTER] and the list is repeated in the second row of the display, but this time without the commas.

📖 *From now on, [2nd] [L1], [2nd] [L2], and so on, will be referred to as L1, L2, and so on.*

Using seq(to Generate Data

An easy way to enter a list of integers (for example, 16 integer values for years of education) is by pasting **seq(** to the home screen as follows.

1. Press [2nd] [LIST], and use ▶ to highlight **OPS** at the top of the first screen, as shown in screen 9.

2. Select **5:seq(**, and then finish the first line as in screen 10. (The easiest way to reach the **X** is by pressing [X,T,Θ,n] to the right of the [ALPHA] key. Press [STO▸] for ➔, and then type **ED** with [ALPHA] **E** [ALPHA] **D**.)

    Press [ENTER].

    Only the first seven integers are displayed, followed by an ellipsis (...). (See second line of screen 10.)

3. Press ▶ and ◀ to scroll the complete list.

Using [2nd] [ENTRY] (Last Entry Feature) and Editing

The integers need not be consecutive as shown in the second example. Build on the example above by using the last entry feature and then using the editing capabilities of [DEL] [2nd] [INS].

1. Press [2nd] [ENTRY] (located above the [ENTER] key) to return the previous entry to the screen; in this case, **seq(X,X,1,16➔ED**.

2. Move the cursor to the **1**, and press [DEL] [DEL] [DEL] [DEL] to delete **1,16**.

3. Press [2nd] [INS].

    The flashing rectangular cursor changes to a flashing underline indicating the insert mode.

4. Type **1790** ⎕ **1990** ⎕**10**, and then press ▶ to jump over the ➔.

5. Press [2nd] [A-LOCK] (above the [ALPHA] key) to set alpha-lock so you can type **YEAR** without pressing [ALPHA] before each letter.

6. Press [ENTER] to get a list of years starting with 1790, 1800, and increasing by ten years up to 1990. (See the last line in screen 10.)

(9)
```
NAMES OPS MATH
1█SortA(
2:SortD(
3:dim(
4:Fill(
5:seq(
6:cumSum(
7↓∆List(
```

(10)
```
seq(X,X,1,16→ED
{1 2 3 4 5 6 7
seq(X,X,1790,199
0,10→YEAR
{1790 1800 1810…
```

Do This First (cont.)

Pasting a List Already Created

1. Press [2nd] [LIST] <NAMES>.

2. Highlight the name, as shown in screen 11. (Your screen will not have all of these names.)

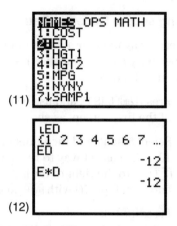

(11)

3. Press [ENTER] to paste the name to the display at the point where you started the process (in this example, the home screen).

   For an example, see the first line of screen 12. Note the small L which indicates this is a list.

4. Press [ENTER] again, and the list is displayed.

(12)

If your list (for example, **YEAR**) is not displayed after you have pressed [2nd] [LIST], you can scroll down the list of names or, if you are at the top of the list, scroll up, which sends you to the bottom of the list of names. However, the best way to find your list name is to press [ALPHA] **Y**. The page with names beginning with Y is displayed. Highlight the correct name (**YEAR**) and press [ENTER] to paste that name.

*Note: Typing **ED** on the home screen without the small L is interpreted as the multiplication of E ∗ D. With your previous entries, this results in a value of -12.*

When pasting a previously created list, the small L will be inserted when needed, so it is safer to paste than type the name when you are not sure if the L is needed.

Entering Data into a List From the Stat Editor (or Spreadsheet)

From the home screen, press [STAT] for the display shown in screen 13.

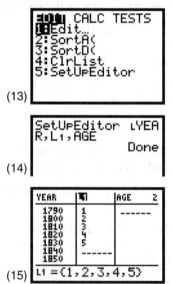

(13)

Using SetUpEditor

With **SetUpEditor**, you can set up the stat list editor to display one or more list names in the order that you specify.

1. Press [STAT] **5:SetUpEditor** to paste **SetUpEditor** to the home screen.

(14)

2. Paste **LYEAR** (from [2nd] [LIST]), press [,] **L₁** [,], and then type the new name, **AGE**, as shown in screen 14.

3. Press [ENTER] for **Done**.

4. Press [STAT] **1:Edit** to reveal the results.

   The spreadsheet should look like screen 15 (however, we have gone one step further by highlighting **L₁** in the top row). List **AGE** was newly created by the above procedure and has no data.

(15)

*Note: Pressing [STAT] **5:SetUpEditor** [ENTER] (without any list) would set up the spreadsheet with six lists, L₁ to L₆. The maximum number of lists in the spreadsheet is 20. The maximum number of list names is limited only by the amount of memory.*

Creating a New List in the Editor

1. Highlight **L1** and press 2nd [INS] to move list **L1** to the right and prompt for a name in the bottom row in alpha-lock mode.

2. Type **PHILY**, and a flashing quilt pattern is displayed, indicating that you have used the maximum word length of five characters . (See screen 16.)

3. Press ENTER ⏷, and then type **548** (the first height given in the table below).

   Screen 17 is displayed.

4. Press ENTER to paste **548** in the first row and move the large rectangular cursor down to the next row.

5. Enter the other 27 values by typing the value and then pressing ENTER.

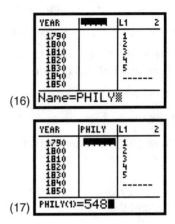

(16)

(17)

Heights (in feet) of Tall Buildings in Philadelphia, PA

548	405	375	400	475	450	412
375	364	492	482	384	490	492
490	435	390	500	400	491	945
435	848	792	700	572	739	572

(Source: Reprinted with permission from the World Almanac and Book of Facts 1996. Copyright © 1995 K-III Reference Corporation. All rights reserved.)

Note: If you had already created list PHILY (with data), then you could have pasted its name next to Name in the second to the last display on the bottom of the previous page. Pressing ENTER then would not only have pasted the name to the top line, but also pasted the data in the rows below the name.

Do This First (cont.)

Editing a List In the Spreadsheet

To check the values of data in a spreadsheet,

1. Press ALPHA ▼ to jump a page at a time down the list.

2. Press ALPHA ▲ to jump a page at a time up the list.

(The green arrows between these cursor control keys are a visual reminder of this function.)

To correct a highlighted value as shown in screen 18,

1. Type the correct value.

2. Press ENTER and the corrected value is pasted to the desired row.

To delete a value,

1. Highlight the value.

2. Press DEL and the value is removed and the rows below it moved up.

To insert a value above another value,

1. Highlight that value.

2. Press 2nd [INS] and the value is moved down and a zero is displayed in the slot above it.

3. Type the correct value in the last row, as in screen 18.

4. Press ENTER and the corrected value replaces the zero.

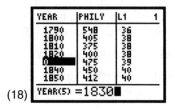

(18)

Clearing a List Of Data

1. From within the spreadsheet, highlight the list name and press CLEAR.
   A display is shown like that in screen 19 with the bottom line cleared.

2. Press ENTER, and the list values are cleared.

You can also use **ClrList.**

1. Press STAT **4:ClrList** to paste **ClrList** to the home screen. Then paste the list to be cleared of data (for example, L1, L2, L3).

2. Press ENTER for **Done**, as in screen 20, with those lists being cleared of data.

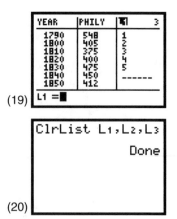

(19)

(20)

Removing a List Name and Data

To remove a list from the spreadsheet,

1. Go to the spreadsheet and highlight the name on the top line.

2. Press DEL.

   The name and the data are gone from the spreadsheet but not from the TI-83 memory.

(21)

To remove both the name and data from memory,

1. Press 2nd [MEM] (above the + key) for the first display, as in screen 21.

2. Select **2:Delete** for a display, as in screen 22.

3. Select **4:List** for a display of list names.

(22)

4. Use ▾ to move the selection cursor to the list you wish to remove (for example, **YEAR**), as in screen 23. Be careful!

5. Press ENTER to remove the list. You can remove lists one by one from this screen.

(23)

6. Press 2nd [QUIT] to return to the home screen.

More On Lists

When storing small data sets, using **L1** to **L6** is convenient. However, when storing large data sets in which you have invested more time, it may be wise to name them.

Large lists can be linked from a computer to a TI-83 or from one TI-83 to another (see the *TI-83 Guidebook* for more information).

Several people can cooperate in keying in large data sets. For example, you can store one part in **L1** on one TI-83 and another part in **L2** on another TI-83. You can share this data by linking the two machines and then combining **L1** and **L2**. You can store results in **L3** by pressing 2nd [LIST] **<OPS> 9:augment(L1** , **L2**) STO▸ **L3**.

Data sets can also be stored in a matrix or transferred from a list to a matrix or from a matrix to a list (see Topics 18 and 48).

📖 *To complete the prerequisites for the activites in this handbook, you now need to cover setting up plots and their windows in Activity 1, Topic 1.*

Activity 1

Describing One-Variable Data

The primary data set you will be working with in this activity is the heights (in feet) of tall buildings in Philadelphia, Pennsylvania. This was stored in list **PHILY** under "Creating a New List in the Editor" in Do This First and was entered in the order of the year completed. The data is duplicated in the table below.

Heights (ft.) of Tall Buildings in Philadelphia, PA

548	405	375	400	475	450	412
375	364	492	482	384	490	492
490	435	390	500	400	491	945
435	848	792	700	572	739	572

(Source: Reprinted with permission from the World Almanac and Book of Facts 1996. Copyright © 1995 K-III Reference Corporation. All rights reserved.)

Topic 1—Histograms and Frequency Tables from Raw Data

Setting up the Plot

1. Press [2nd] [STAT PLOT] **1:Plot1** [ENTER] to display screen 1. (Your screen may have **Off** highlighted.)

2. Turn on the plot by pressing [ENTER] with the flashing cursor on **On. On** will now be highlighted instead of **Off**.

3. Use ▼ to move down to **Type**.

    The cursor flashes on the first type, **Scatter** plot ⌐. Starting from the first type, pressing ▶ moves to the other five types: **xyLine** ⌐, **Histogram** ⊞ , **Modified Boxplot** ⊡, **Boxplot** ⊞ (regular box plot), and **Normal Probability** plot ⌐.

4. Press ▶ ▶ to move to **Histogram**, the third type, and then press [ENTER] to select it.

5. Use ▼ to move down to the input request **Xlist**. (Note that the input request depends on the plot type selected.)

    Paste the list **PHILY**, and set **Freq** to **1** (because this is raw data, and you will count each value once).

(1)

Activity 1, Describing One-Variable Data (cont.)

Using the Automatic Window

Press ZOOM **9:ZoomStat** TRACE followed by several ▶ for the display of the **Histogram** in screen 2. Notice that the lower class limit for the rightmost class is **min = 945**. There is only **n = 1** value in this last cell indicating the tallest building is 945 feet. The class width is a bit strange, but it is nice to have this automatic plot capability.

Setting Up the Window

1. Press WINDOW for screen 3, which reveals that the shortest building (**Xmin**) is **364** feet.

2. Change the values, as shown in screen 4, to include all values with reasonable class limits and class width (**Xscl =100**). Making **Ymin** the negative of **Ymax/4** leaves enough room at the bottom of the plot screen for the class information.

3. Press TRACE for screen 5 with 11 buildings in the first height class. Using ▶ reveals frequencies of **10, 2, 2, 2,** and **1** for the other classes.

The Frequency Table

The values shown in step 3 (above) make up the *frequency table* given below.

Class Limits	Frequency
350 to < 450	11
450 to < 550	10
550 to < 650	2
650 to < 750	2
750 to < 850	2
850 to < 950	1

The Effect of Changing Class Width or Xscl

If you change the **WINDOW** in screen 4 so that the class width is **Xscl = 20**, press TRACE, and then ▶, you obtain the cell that identifies the Philadelphia City Hall at 548 feet (see screen 6). (The City Hall height includes the 37-foot statue of William Penn. Until 1987 (by plan), no buildings were higher than the City Hall.)

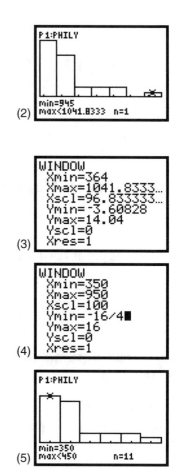

(2)

(3)

(4)

(5)

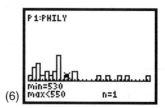

(6)

If you change the window in screen 4 so that **Xscl = 150**, and then press TRACE, you find that with 19 values in the first class, its rectangle does not fit the display (see screen 7). The values of **Ymin** and **Ymax** must be adjusted. (One way that works is **Ymin = -6** and **Ymax = 24**.)

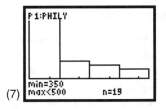

(7)

Topic 2—Histograms from Frequency and Relative Frequency Tables

A frequency table for the heights (in feet) of tall buildings in Philadelphia, PA is given below with 11 buildings from 350 up to 450 feet and only one building 850 feet or taller.

Class Limits	Frequency
350 to < 450	11
450 to < 550	10
550 to < 650	2
650 to < 750	2
750 to < 850	2
850 to < 950	1

Calculating Class Marks

1. Store the lower class limits in **L1** and the upper class limits in **L2** in the stat editor.

2. Highlight **L3** at the top of the spreadsheet, and type (**L1** + **L2**) ÷ **2**, as shown in the bottom line in screen 8.

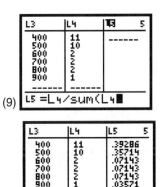

(8)

3. Press ENTER to reveal the class marks in **L3** (see screen 9 where the frequencies also have been added to **L4**).

Calculating Relative Frequencies

1. Highlight **L5** at the top of the spreadsheet , as shown in screen 9.

(9)

2. Enter **L4** ÷ 2nd [LIST] <MATH> 5:sum(**L4**, as shown in the bottom line in screen 9.

3. Press ENTER and the relative frequencies are placed in **L5**, as shown in screen 10, with **39.29** percent of the buildings in the first class.

(10)

Activity 1, Describing One-Variable Data (cont.)

Setting Up Plot and Window

Set up **Plot1** for a **Histogram** as shown in screen 11 with the
WINDOW as shown in screen 12, where
Xmin = 350, the lower limit of the first class
Xmax = 950, the upper limit of the last class
Xscl = 100, the class width or the distance between the class
marks
Ymax = 16 gives room for the maximum frequency of 11, plus
extra room for labels at the top of the **Histogram**.

The Frequency Histogram

Pressing TRACE reveals the frequency **Histogram** displayed in
screen 13.

The *relative frequency Histogram* is given in screen 16 (with
the setup in screens 14 and 15) with **n = .3929** percent of the
buildings in the first class. (Note that the **Freq** input is actually
the relative frequencies in **L5**.)

Topic 3—Stem-and-Leaf Plots and Dot Plots

The stem-and-leaf plot and dot plot are easy to make by hand if
the data is in order.

1. Make a copy of the list **PHILY** (the Philadelphia, PA
    building heights that you saved. See the first page of
    Activity 1) by storing it in **L4**.

2. From the home screen, paste **LPHILY** and press STO▶ **L4**;
    or, from the spreadsheet, highlight **L4** in the top line,
    paste **LPHILY** in the bottom line, and press ENTER.

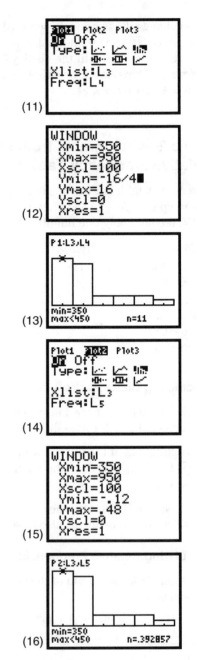

(11)

(12)

(13)

(14)

(15)

(16)

Putting Data In Order

Sort the values in ascending order from low to high value by pressing [STAT] **2:SortA(L4** [ENTER]. **Done** is displayed, as shown in screen 17.

Stem-and Leaf Plot

Entering the stat editor reveals the data for easy reading. The first seven values shown in screen 18, when rounded to the nearest ten and given in tens, are **36, 38, 38, 38, 39, 40, 40**. These values start the stem-and-leaf plot shown below. The complete plot is given below the start-up plot with data from St.Louis.

3|68889
4|00

St. Louis   Philadelphia
     98| 3 |68889
   320| 4 |00114458899999
  994| 5 |0577
    3| 6 |
     | 7 |049
     | 8 |5
     | 9 |5

St. Louis, Missouri has nine buildings over 350 feet tall as follows.

375 390 398 420 434 540 588 593 630
(Source: Reprinted with permission from the World Almanac and Book of Facts 1996. Copyright © 1995 K-III Reference Corporation. All rights reserved.)

Above is the complete back-to-back stem-and-leaf plots for the two data sets. St. Louis has a fairly symmetric distribution of tall building heights with no buildings taller than 630 feet (the arch). Philadelphia has many more tall buildings with a distribution skewed to taller values. Until 1986, however,when the seven tallest buildings were built in Philadelphia, St. Louis had the taller buildings.

Dot Plot

With the data in order, a dot plot is easy to construct by hand with one dot for each building above its height scale value, but it can also be plotted easily on the TI-83.

1. Highlight **L5**, as shown in the top line of screen 18.

2. Press [MATH] **<NUM> 2:round(L4** [÷] **10** [,] **0** [)]**, as shown in the bottom line of screen 18.

(17)

(18)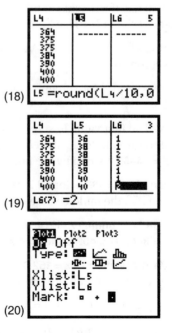

(19)

(20)

3. Press ENTER for the heights of the buildings to the nearest 10 feet (given in tens), as shown in screen 19.

4. In **L6**, type the counting numbers next to each height in **L5**. There is **1** value of **36**, but **1, 2, 3** values of **38**, and so on, as shown in screen 19.

5. Set up **Plot1** for a **Scatter** plot (the first type), as shown in screen 20.

6. Set up the **WINDOW** as shown in screen 21.

7. Press TRACE and then ▶ a few times for screen 22, which shows there are five buildings approximately 490 feet tall in Philadelphia.

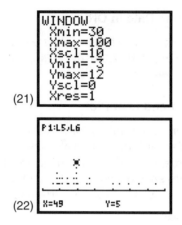

(21)

(22)

Topic 4—Measures of Central Tendency and Variability

The most common measures of central tendency (the *mean* and the *median*) and measures of spread or variability of a distribution (the *standard deviation, variance, interquartile range,* and *five-number summary*) are given for both a list of raw data and for data grouped in a frequency table.

Using Raw Data

You will use the heights of tall Philadelphia buildings as stored in list **LPHILY** in Do This First.

1. Press STAT <CALC> 1:1-Var Stats **LPHILY** to display screen 23.

2. Press ENTER for screen 24, and then use ▼ to see screen 25.

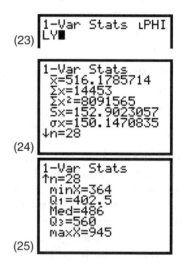

(23)

(24)

(25)

mean - The first value in screen 24 is x̄ = **516.1785714**, which is equal to the sum of the data (the second value of the output), or Σx = **14453** divided by the number of data values, or **n = 28**.

median - **Med = 486** is found in the second screen of the output (screen 25), the middle value of the five-number summary.

five-number summary - From the second screen of the output, **minX = 364, Q1 = 402.5, Med = 486, Q3 = 560, maxX = 945.**

standard deviation - **Sx = 152.902** and **σx = 150.147** are the last values of the first output screen above **n**. (See screen 24.)

$$Sx = \sqrt{(\Sigma(x - \bar{x})^2)/(n - 1)} = \sqrt{((\Sigma x^2 - (\Sigma x)^2/n)/(n - 1))}$$

$$\sigma x = \sqrt{((\Sigma (x - \mu)^2)/n)} = \sqrt{((\Sigma x^2 - (\Sigma x)^2/n)/n)}$$

Note: Because the set of interest is a population of the heights of all the tall buildings in Philadelphia (not a sample of heights), the mean is usually signified as μ but its calculation and value are the same as x̄.

Note: Because the set of interest is a population of the heights of all the tall buildings in Philadelphia (not a sample of heights), σx is appropriate (Sx is used to estimate σx from a sample).

interquartile range - It is easy enough to calculate the interquartile range from **Q3 - Q1 = 157.5**, as shown in the first two lines of screen 26.

variance - It is a bit tedious to calculate the variance by typing in the digits of the standard deviation and then squaring it using x^2. You may want to paste σx by pressing VARS **5:Statistics <XY> 4: σx** and then squaring this, as shown in the last two lines of screen 26.

If your data was a sample from a larger population, you could calculate the sample variance (division by **n-1**) in a similar way with VARS **5:Statistics <XY> 3:Sx**. Another possibility is to press 2nd [LIST] **<MATH> 8:variance(ʟPHILY**, as shown in the last two lines of screen 27. This gives the same answer, **23379.11508**.

Using Grouped Data

You will use the frequency table of the Philadelphia data as grouped in Topic 2, including the class marks below. The class marks are stored in **L3** and the frequencies in **L4**. (See screen 28.)

Class Limits	Class Mark	Frequency
350 to < 450	400	11
450 to < 550	500	10
550 to < 650	600	2
650 to < 750	700	2
750 to < 850	800	2
850 to < 950	900	1

1. Press STAT **<CALC> 1:1-Var Stats L3** ⦁ **L4** for screen 29.

2. Press ENTER and then use ⦁ to see screens 30 and 31.

   The output is similar to the raw data output because basically, it comes from the same data. However, instead of 11 different values from 350 up to 449, you treat all 11 values as 400. Likewise, the largest value is treated as 900 instead of the actual 945. A mean of **517.9** feet for the grouped data compared to the actual **516.2** (in screen 24) feet is not bad.

If the actual data is such that there are in fact eleven 400s, ten 500s, two 600s, two 700s, two 800s, and one 900, then the output using the grouped procedure above is correct and not an approximation.

If you have the raw data, it makes sense to use it. But if you only have a table of grouped data to summarize raw data, this is the option to use.

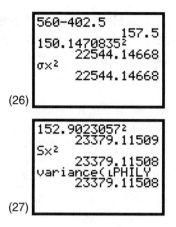

(26)

(27)

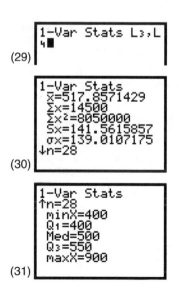

(28)

(29)

(30)

(31)

Topic 5—Measures of Position and Cumulative Relative Frequency Distributions (Ogives): Percentiles and Quartiles, Standard Scores (z-scores)

You will work with the heights (in feet) of tall Philadelphia buildings that you stored in list **LPHILY** in Do This First. This data is duplicated at the beginning of Activity 1.

```
(364-516.18)/150
.15
           -1.013519814
(945-516.18)/150
.15
            2.855944056
```
(32)

Finding Standard scores (z-scores)

Standard scores (z scores) are numbers that represent how many standard deviations X is above or below the mean, or $z = (X - \mu)/\sigma x$.

From Topic 4 you found the mean = μ = **516.18**, and the standard deviation = σx = **150.15**. Use these values to find the z score of the smallest (364 feet) and the tallest (945 feet) buildings in your list. (See screen 32.)

Smallest Building: z = **(364 - 516.18)/150.15 = -1.01**
Largest Building: z = **(945 - 516.18)/150.15 = +2.86**

The 2nd [ENTRY] (last entry) feature works nicely here. Pasting μ and σx (as shown in Topic 4) is also a possibility.

The smallest value is about one standard deviation below the mean, and the largest value is almost three standard deviations above the mean. This indicates the non-symmetric nature of the distribution (it is skewed to the right).

Finding Percentiles and Quartiles

The *percentile* of a score indicates what percent of the data values are less in magnitude. Not all textbooks use the same procedure for finding percentiles, but all methods give similar answers as the list size increases.

The first quartile is the same as the twenty-first percentile (**Q1= P25**); also **Q3 = P75**, and the median is the same as **P50**. These three values are part of the five-number summary obtained with STAT <CALC> 1:1-Var Stats **LPHILY**, as shown in Topic 4, with **Q1 = 402.5, Med = 486, Q3 = 560** and **n = 28**.

---

1. Put the **PHILY** data in order in **L5** (from smallest to largest value) as was done in Topic 3.

2. Find **P40** and **P75** (remember **n = 28**).

   P40: $0.40 * 28 = 11.2$. Round up to 12. The twelfth value of **L5** or **L5(12) = 450**, as shown in screen 33.

   P75: $0.75 * 28 = 21$. Because this is an integer, take the mean of the twenty-first and twenty-second values, as shown in the display (**Q3 = 560**).

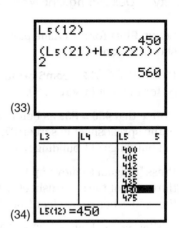

(33)

(34)

Given a value of 450 feet for a building's height, what percentile value is this in your list?

Going down the list in the stat list editor, you find this is the twelfth value, as shown in screen 34, so there are 11 tall buildings less than 450 feet. Because $11/28 = 0.393$, this is approximately **P39**. Because you found **P40 = 450** (above) and now have **P39 = 450**, at least one percentile value is indeed approximate, but these two values would be closer as the size of the data list increased.

Finding Cumulative Relative Frequency Distributions (Ogives) and Percentiles

Using the frequency tables of the building heights in Topic 2 (at right), do the following.

Class Limits	Frequency
350 to < 450	11
450 to < 550	10
550 to < 650	2
650 to < 750	2
750 to < 850	2
850 to < 950	1

1. Put the lower class limits and the last upper class limit in **L1**.

2. Put the frequencies in **L2**, but with the first value being an extra value zero. (See screen 35.)

3. Highlight **L3** and paste **cumSum(L2**, as shown in the last line of screen 35. (**cumSum** from [2nd] [LIST] **<OPS> 6**).

4. Press [ENTER] for screen 36 with the cumulative frequencies in **L3**.

5. Highlight **L4** and put **L3** [÷] **28**, as shown in the last line of screen 36.

6. Press [ENTER] for screen 37 with the cumulative relative frequencies in **L4**.

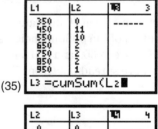

(35)

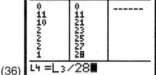

(36)

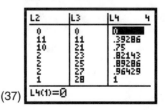

(37)

Activity 1, Describing One-Variable Data (cont.)

7. Set up **Plot1** for an **xyLine** plot (the second type), as shown in screen 38.

8. Plot with ZOOM **9:ZoomStat**, and then press TRACE and ▶ for the plot in screen 39.

   Notice that **450 = P39** as before and in the second row of the spreadsheet in screen 37. About 39 percent of the tall buildings (11 buildings) are less than 450 feet.

9. Press ▶ again to move up to the next point and the third row of the spreadsheet with 21 or 75 percent of the values below 550 feet (the third quartile).

   Earlier, you calculated **Q3 = 560** feet (the mean of the twenty-first and twenty-second value). Again, as the sample size increases (such as the results of the Scholastic Aptitude Test (SAT) where all values are represented), these differences will diminish.

10. To approximate other values that are not points in the spreadsheet, press GRAPH, and then the cursor control keys to move the cross hairs as close to the desired point as possible.

The example in screen 40 approximates **P50** as 481 compared to the previous value of 486. You are limited by using straight lines to connect points, but this limitation is reduced as the data set and number of points increase. You are also limited by technology and the width of a pixel.

The ogive in screen 40 indicates the skewed nature of the distribution of the building heights. The slope is very steep up to **P75** (between 350 and 550 feet), but the top 25 percent of the data is more spread out (from 550 to 950 feet).

(38)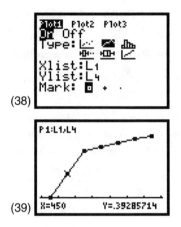

(39)

(40)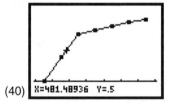

Topic 6—Box Plots and Five-Number Summary

You will start with the heights (in feet) of tall Philadelphia buildings stored in list **LPHILY** in Do This First. This data is duplicated at the beginning of Activity 1.

Setting up Box plots

1. Set up **Plot1** for a **Modified Boxplot** (the fourth type), as shown in screen 41. It is called modified to distinguish it from the next choice, a regular box plot , called just **Boxplot**.

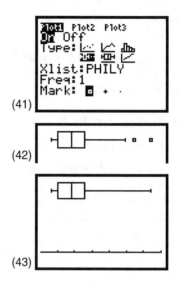

(41)

(42)

2. Press ZOOM **9:ZoomStat** for screen 42. If you were set up for a regular **Boxplot**, you would get the next display in screen 43. The only difference is that the right "whisker" (these are also sometimes called "box and whisker" plots) is extended out to the maximum value.

(43)

Calculating a Five-Number Summary

1. Press TRACE and the median shows a flashing box and value of **486** at the bottom of the screen.

2. Press ◄ and you have **Q1 = 402.5**.

    Press ◄ again and you have **minX = 364**.

3. Go in the other direction and you find **Q3 = 560**, and then skip all the way to the right box for **maxX = 945**.

These make up the five-number summary of data, which was also covered in Topic 4 and available from the second screen of STAT <CALC> **1:1-Var Stats LPHILY**.

The two points skipped were **X = 792** (shown in screen 44) and **X = 848**, the third and second largest values. You separated the top two values from the whiskers to identify them as possible "outliers," values that are far away from the rest of the data and that may have a special story.

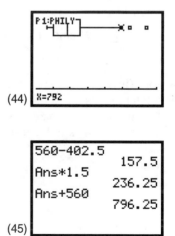

(44)

(To separate these points, take **Q1 - 1.5 ∗ IQR** and **Q3 + 1.5 ∗ IQR**, where **IQR** stands for the interquartile range or **IQR = Q3 - Q1 = 560 - 402.5 = 157.5** (as shown in Topic 4). Thus, **1.5 ∗ IQR = 1.5 ∗ 157.5 = 236.25** and **Q3 + 236.25 = 796.25**. (See screen 45.) The first value below 796.25 is 792, but 848 and 945 are above it. **Q1 - 236.25 = 166.25,** and none of the buildings in our list were less than that; therefore, no possible outliers are identified off to the left.)

(45)

Activity 1, Describing One-Variable Data (cont.)

Box Plot with Histogram

After setting up **Plot1** as above in screen 40, set up **Plot2** for a **Histogram** as shown in screen 46 and **WINDOW** as shown in screen 47.

Pressing GRAPH gives screen 48. The added **Histogram** (as shown in Topic 1) indicates you might want to treat the five upper values as special.

Side-By-Side Box Plots

Up to three box plots can be plotted on the same screen.

The 28 tallest buildings in New York, New York are stored in list **NYNY** and listed below. (Twenty-eight buildings were identified as tall in Philadelphia. In New York City, 131 buildings were so identified.)

ʟ**NYNY:** 700 705 707 716 724 725 730 739 741 743 745 750 750 752 757 778 792 808 813 814 850 915 927 950 1046 1414 1362 1368

(Source: Reprinted with permission from the World Almanac and Book of Facts 1996. Copyright © 1995 K-III Reference Corporation. All rights reserved.)

Nine buildings are identified as tall in St. Louis, Missouri. The heights are stored in ʟ**STLOU.**

ʟ**STLOU:** 375 390 398 420 434 540 588 593 630

1. Set up all three plots as **Modified Boxplots**, as shown in screen 49.

2. Press ZOOM **9:ZoomStat** for the next display (screen 50).

3. Press TRACE and ⊡ to investigate the different plots.

New York (in the middle) is the city of skyscrapers, and Philadelphia seems much more like St. Louis. Because of the difference in sample size, it is easier to make this later comparison with back-to-back stem-and-leaf plots, as shown in Topic 3.

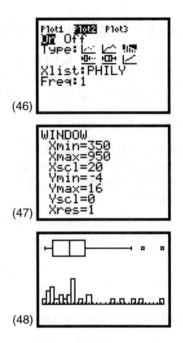

(46)

(47)

(48)

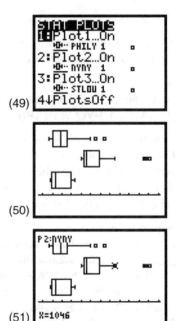

(49)

(50)

(51)

Activity 2

Describing Bivariate Data (Two Quantitative Variables)

Several types of *x-y* plots will demonstrate the relationship between two quantitative variables. By using different symbols, relationships for several categories can be compared on the same plot. The correlation coefficient will be calculated to measure the strength and direction of the linear relationship between the two variables.

Topic 7—Scatter Plots

Some World Indoor Track records (as of Oct. 1, 1995) are given in the table below and stored in **L1** and **L2**.

	Men				Women			
L1: meters	200	400	800	1000	200	400	800	1000
L2: seconds	20.3	45.0	104.8	135.2	21.8	49.5	116.4	154.8

(Source: Reprinted with permission from The World Almanac and Book of Facts 1996. Copyright © 1995 K-III Reference Corporation. All rights reserved.)

1. Press [2nd] [STAT PLOT] **1:Plot1,** and set up the plot for a **Scatter** plot (the first type), as shown in screen 1.

2. With **Xscl = 200** under **WINDOW**, press [ZOOM] **9:ZoomStat** [TRACE], and then a few [▶] for the plot in screen 2.

   You see two different times for each race distance except the 200-meter race. The relatively small difference between the times does not show on the plot because they turn on the same pixel.

(1)

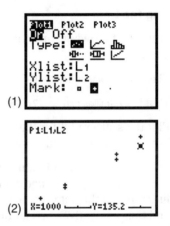

(2)

Note: [ZOOM] *9:ZoomStat will result in a DIM MISMATCH Error if your Xlist and Ylist are of unequal length and a WINDOW RANGE Error if your Xlist or Ylist are all the same value. In the first case, correct your list so that only pairs of x,y values have been entered. In the second case, if you still wish to plot, you must set your window by hand so Xmin ≠ Xmax and Ymin ≠ Ymax.*

Adding Categories

(Gender indicated by **Mark** type)

1. Store distances in **L1**, men's times in **L2**, and women's times in **L3** (see screen 3).

2. Leave **Plot1** on as above, and turn on **Plot2** with a different **Mark** type (see screen 4).

3. Press TRACE and a few ▶ for screen 5 with a square for women and a cross for men.

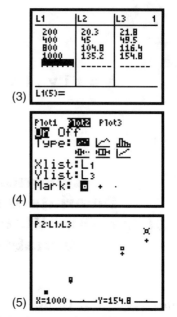

Topic 8—Correlation and Linearity

You will measure the strength of a linear relationship in this section and then save fitting a straight line to the data for Topics 11 and 15.

Plotting the Data

1. Store the following automobile gas mileage data into **L1** and **L2**.

    Xlist in **L1**: (horsepower)   75   80   85   100   125   135   160   175

    Ylist in **L2**: (milles/gal)   27   25   15   22   19   16   10   12

2. Plot the scatter plot for the above data as shown in Topic 7 with results like that in screen 6.

    There is an inverse relationship in that as horsepower increases, the gas mileage decreases. If you fit a straight line through the data, it would have a negative slope and thus a negative correlation coefficient.

Turning on the Diagnostic Flag

If you have have not turned on the diagnostic flag since your TI-83 was reset, do the following.

1. Press 2nd [CATALOG] (above the numeral zero) to display screen 7, which is in alpha mode (note **A** in the upper-right corner).

2. Press **D** and use ▼ to move the pointer to **DiagnosticOn**, as shown in screen 8.

3. Press ENTER to paste **DiagnosticOn** to the home screen, and then press ENTER for **Done** (see the first two lines in screen 9).

Note: In general, the Xlist need not be the same for the two plots.

Obtaining the Correlation Coefficient

1. Press STAT <CALC> 4:LinReg(ax+b) L1 , L2 for the third and fourth lines of screen 9.

2. Press ENTER for screen 10 with a correlation coefficient of **r = -.8229**.

More Scatter

1. Return to the tall building data originally found in Do This First and stored in list **PHILY** in the order of the year in which the buildings were completed. Those years are given below in the same order. Put these values in a list called **YRPHI**.

   1901 1927 1928 1929 1930 1930 1930
   1931 1931 1932 1968 1970 1970 1972
   1973 1973 1973 1974 1982 1983 1987
   1987 1989 1989 1990 1990 1991 1992

2. Plot the **Scatter** plot as shown in Topic 7 and in screens 11 through 12.

Notice that the City Hall (at 548 feet) was completed in 1901 (the oldest building) and that no building topped that height until 1987. In 1992, five buildings stood taller than City Hall. Also note that after City Hall, no other tall buildings were built until a cluster of nine around 1930 and another cluster around 1970.

The scatter is not very linear as you can see from the scatter and the low value of **r = .523** and **r^2 = .273**.

Topic 9—Time Plots

You will see how a variable changes with time by plotting time on the x-axis and the variable of interest on the y-axis. Points are usually joined by lines, and thus you will use the TI-83 **xyLine** plots.

The following data is men's Olympic Marathon times.

Year in L1:	1900	1920	1936	1960	1980
Hours in L2:	2.996	2.543	2.489	2.255	2.184

(Source: Reprinted with permission from The World Almanac and Book of Facts 1996. Copyright © 1995 K-III Reference Corporation. All rights reserved.)

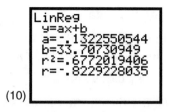

(10)

*Note: If r^2 and **r** do not show on your screen, then the diagnostic flag is off and must be turned on as explained on the previous page.*

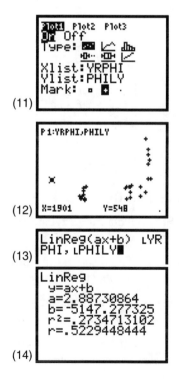

(11)

(12)

(13)

(14)

Plotting the Data

1. Press [2nd] [STAT PLOT] **1:Plot1**, and set up for an **xyLine** plot (the second plot type), **as shown in** screen 15.

2. Press [ZOOM] **9:ZoomStat** [TRACE] for the plot in screen 16.

   Notice that the time it takes to run the marathon is decreasing but at a decreasing rate.

Topic 10—Control Charts

Given the following sample means with UCL = 6.515, Center Line = 6.500, and LCL = 6.485, you will plot the X-bar control chart. Other control charts can be plotted similarly.

Sample Num L₁	Sample Mean L₂
1	6.507
2	6.503
3	6.498
4	6.501
5	6.495
6	6.501
7	6.494
8	6.497
9	6.509
10	6.505

Plotting the Data

1. Set up **Plot1** for an **xyLine** plot as shown in Topic 9 and as shown in screen 17.

2. Press [Y=] and set up the editor as shown in screen 18. (Note that **Plot1** must be on).

3. Press [ZOOM] **9:ZoomStat** for screen 19, which includes all points but not the control limits.

   Adjust the window as shown in screen 20, and press [TRACE] for the complete control chart shown in screen 21.

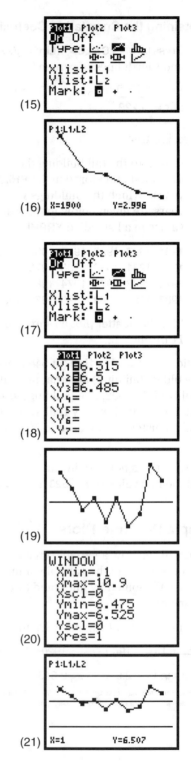

(15)

(16)

(17)

(18)

(19)

(20)

(21)

EXPLORATIONS

Activity 3

Fitting an Equation to Bivariate Data

In this activity, you will start by fitting a linear least-squares regression line in Topic 11 to the U.S. Census data given on the next page. This will set the stage for the activities that follow.

The shape of the resulting curve looks like part of a parabola (a quadratic equation), which is one of the polynomial regression fits discussed in Topic 12 (cubic and quadrinomial fits being the others).

Population models suggest exponential or logistic growth as possible fits. Exponential growth will be discussed in Topic 13 as a fit that uses a transformation of data to make it more linear (logarithmic and power fits are the others). The logistic fit (which is our selection for the best fit) is covered in Topic 14.

Topic 15 returns to fitting a straight line to data , but by a technique that is more resistant to unusual values (median-median fit) than the least-squares fit of Topic 11.

Topic 16 fits a trigonometric sine curve to periodic data.

Note that if your fit display screens are different from those shown in this activity (do not show r, r^2 or R^2 when this handbook does) your diagnostic flag is off. Topic 8 shows how to turn it on.

📖 *Read Topic 11 before reading other topics in Activity 3.*

Setting Up

The main data set for this activity is the U.S. Census data (in millions of people) given on the next page. Store it in list **USPOP** with a coded year value of 1 to 18 for the years 1810 to 1980 in list **L₁** . The value for 1990 is 249.63 million people, but you do not include this in the list because you will use it to check how well the fit equation can predict it.

Activity 3, Fitting an Equation to Bivariate Data (cont.)

YEAR:	1810	1820	1830	1840	1850	1860	1870	1880	1890
L₁ **X:**	1	2	3	4	5	6	7	8	9
USPOP **Y:**	7.24	9.64	12.87	17.07	23.19	31.44	39.82	50.16	62.95
YEAR:	1900	1910	1920	1930	1940	1950	1960	1970	1980
X:	10	11	12	13	14	15	16	17	18
Y:	75.99	91.97	105.71	122.78	131.67	151.33	179.32	203.21	226.5

1. Set up **Plot1** for a **Scatter** plot, as shown in Topic 7 and in screen 1.

2. Press $\boxed{\text{ZOOM}}$ **9: ZoomStat** $\boxed{\text{TRACE}}$ to produce the plot of your data, as shown in screen 2.

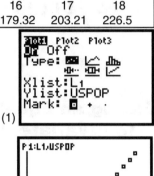
(1)

The top of the plot screen shows the setup with **P1:L₁,USPOP**. The points seem to lie more on a curve than a straight line, but you will start with fitting the linear least-squares regression line (Topic 11) to the data to set the stage and understand the notation for the activities that follow.

(2)

Topic 11—Linear Least Squares Regression Line

The following procedure obtains a linear least squares regression line.

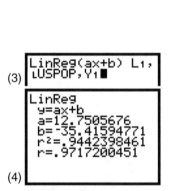
(3)

1. Calculate the fit equation.

   a. Press $\boxed{\text{STAT}}$ **<CALC> 4:LinReg(ax + b) L₁** $\boxed{,}$ **ʟUSPOP** $\boxed{,}$ **Y1**, as shown in screen 3, with **Y1** pasted from $\boxed{\text{VARS}}$ **<Y-VARS> 1:Function 1:Y1**.

   b. Press $\boxed{\text{ENTER}}$ for screen 4 showing your linear fit **Y1 = 12.751x - 35.416** stored in **Y1** in the Y= editor.

(4)

Note: You would get the same results with $\boxed{\text{STAT}}$ **<CALC> 8:LinReg(a + bx) L₁** $\boxed{,}$ **ʟUSPOP** $\boxed{,}$ **Y1** but the slope would be **b** instead of **a**.

2. Plot data scatter and fit equation.

   a. Keeping **Y1** turned on (this was done automatically in step 1), turn on **Plot1** as a **Scatter** plot (as shown in Topic 7) with all other Y= functions and stat plots turned off.

   b. Press $\boxed{\text{ZOOM}}$ **9:ZoomStat** $\boxed{\text{TRACE}}$ for both a **Scatter** plot of the data and a plot of the regression line, as shown in screen 5.

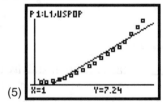
(5)

3. Plot residuals.

   Step 1 automatically stores the residuals in list **RESID**.

   a. Set up **Plot2** as a **Scatter** plot with **Xlist:L1** and **Ylist:RESID** (making sure all other stat plots and Y= plots are off).

   b. Press $\boxed{\text{ZOOM}}$ **9:ZoomStat** $\boxed{\text{TRACE}}$ for screen 6.

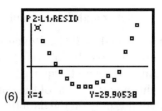

(6)

   The non-random pattern of the **Scatter** plot of residuals confirms that the linear least squares regression line does not fit the data very well. Note that the pattern looks quadratic.

   The *residual* is the difference from the actual y-value and the value obtained by plugging the x-value that goes with the y-value into the regression equation. When $x = 1$, you have **Y1** = $12.751x$ - 35.416, which becomes **Y1**(1) = 12.751(1) - 35.416 = - **22.665**. The difference from the actual value of 7.24 is **7.24** minus **-22.665**, or **29.905**.

   When you paste list **RESID** to the home screen (as shown in the last two lines of screen 7), you confirm this calculation.

Note: For a perfect fit, the residuals will be all zero and $\boxed{\text{ZOOM}}$ 9:ZoomStat will result in a WINDOW RANGE error since Ymin = 0 Ymax = 0. If you still wish to see the plot, change Ymin = -1 and Ymax = 1 and then press $\boxed{\text{TRACE}}$.

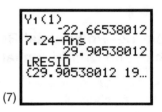

(7)

4. Measure the fit (SSE).

   With some residuals positive, some negative, and some possibly zero, you will use the Sum of the Squared Residual Errors (SSE) as your measure of how close the points fit the curve. (If all the points are on the curve, this would be zero.) SSE is calculated in screen 8, where SSE = **4651.51534**, with **sum** pasted from $\boxed{\text{2nd}}$ [LIST] <MATH> 5:sum.

(8)

5. Predict the population in 1990 ($X = 19$).

   a. Paste **Y1** to the home screen, and then type $\boxed{(}$ 19 $\boxed{)}$, as shown on the first line in screen 9.

   b. Press $\boxed{\text{ENTER}}$ for the next line, which is the predicted value of **Y**, or **206.845**.

      Because you know the actual census value was 249.63, you can calculate the difference. The difference is **42.78516**, or 17 percent, a fairly large error. (See the calculations in screen 9. Note **Ans** is from $\boxed{\text{2nd}}$ [ANS] in the last row of the keyboard.)

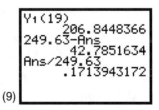

(9)

6. Calculate **r** and r^2 as measure of linearity.

    r^2 is related to SSE in the current case. To show this, you need to calculate the Sum of Squares Total (SST); that is, the sum to squared differences for each y data value and the mean of the complete **Y** list. (SST depends only on the data list and is independent of the fit equation used.)

    SST = **sum(** 〔⒧ **ʟUSPOP** ⒧–⒧ **mean** 〔⒧ **ʟUSPOP** ⒧⟩⒧⟩
    x^2 ⒧⟩ = **83420.06** with the mean pasted from 2nd [LIST]
    <MATH> 3:mean. r^2 = 1 – SSE/SST = **0.9442** as before and in screen 10.

(10)

Note: Small residuals (SEE) give an r^2 close to one. Large residuals (SEE) give an r^2 close to zero.

Topic 12—Polynomial Regression: Quadratic, Cubic, and Quadrinomial

Press STAT <CALC> to reveal screen 11. This topic covers the last three functions shown.

5:QuadReg fits $Y = ax^2 + bx + c$
6:CubicReg fits $Y = ax^3 + bx^2 + cx + d$
7:QuartReg fits $Y = ax^4 + bx^3 + cx^2 + dx + e$

Quadratic Fit

In this procedure, you will fit the quadratic equation to the population census data. The procedure for the other fits is the same.

Note that the numbers of the steps below refer to the steps in Topic 11 that present more detail.

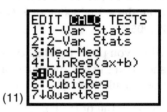

(11)

Step in Topic 11	Display
1. *Calculate the fit equation.*	Press STAT <CALC> **5:QuadReg L1** 〔,〕 **ʟUSPOP** 〔,〕 **Y1** (with **Y1** pasted from VARS <Y-VARS> **1:Function 1:Y1**) for screen 12. Press ENTER for screen 13. Note that R^2 = **0.9984** compared to r^2 = **0.9442** for the linear regression in Topic 11.
2. *Plot data scatter and fit equation*	The regression plot through the data appears to fit very well. (See screen 14.)

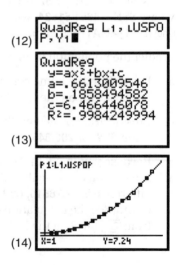

(12)

(13)

(14)

(cont.) **Step in Topic 11**	**Display**

3. *Plot residuals.* The residual plot appears more random than that in Topic 11. (See screen 15.)

(15)

4. *Measure the fit (SSE).* As shown in screen 16, SSE = **131.387** for the quadratic fit compared to **4651.515** in Topic 11.

(16)

5. *Predict population in 1990 (X = 19).* The prediction for 1990 $(X = 19)$ is off by less than 1 percent (**0.36** percent). (See screen 17.)

(17)

6. *Calculate r and r^2 as measure of linearity.* Note that SSE is directly related to R^2 for this multiple linear least squares fit as it was to r^2 before for the "simple" linear least squares fit. ($Y = ax^2 + bx + c = a\,X_2 + bX_1 + c$ is linear in the coefficient a, b, and c with $X_2 = (X_1)^2$.) (See screen 18.)

(18)

Topic 13— Fits Linear by Transformations: Logarithmic, Exponential, and Power Regression

Press $\boxed{\text{STAT}}$ **<CALC>** and then $\boxed{\blacktriangledown}$ a few times to reveal screen 19. This section discusses the last three functions shown.

9: LnReg Fits $y = a + b(\ln x) = a + b\,X$ (linear in a and b). Calculates a and b using linear least squares on lists of $\ln x$ and y instead of x and y.

(19)

0: ExpReg Fits $y = a * b^x = a * b^x$. Transforms to $(\ln y) = (\ln a) + (\ln b)x = A + Bx$ (not linear in a and b). Calculates A and B using linear least squares on list of x and $\ln y$ instead of x and y, then a $= e^A$ and $b = e^B$.

A: PwrReg Fits $y = a * x^b = \text{a} * x^\text{b}$ Transforms to $(\ln y) = (\ln a) + b(\ln x) = A + bX$ (not linear in a and b). Calculates A and b using linear least squares on list of $\ln x$ and $\ln y$ instead of x and y, then $a = e^A$.

Exponential Fit

You will fit the exponential equation to the population census data; however, the procedure for the other fits is the same.

Note that the numbers of the steps below refer to the steps in Topic 11 that present more detail.

Step in Topic 11	Display
1. *Calculate the fit equation.*	Press STAT <CALC> 0:ExpReg L1 ⃞ LUSPOP ⃞ Y1 ENTER for screens 20 and 21
	It is best to turn off the diagnostic flag (see Topic 8) here because **r** and **r²** pertain to the transformed equation above and not to the fit equation in screen 21.
4. *Measure the fit (SSE).*	As shown in screen 22,
6. *Calculate **r** and **r²** as measure of linearity.*	SSE = **9848.987**, but there is no relationship between this and **r²** (**.8819** ≠ **.9695**)
2. *Plot data scatter and fit equation.*	As you can see in screens 22 and 24, the exponential curve does not fit well. The residual plot shows the unfortunate pattern of larger errors as time progresses.
3. *Plot residuals.*	
5. *Predict population in 1990 (X = 19).*	Screen 25 shows an error of **-48.3** percent for 1990.

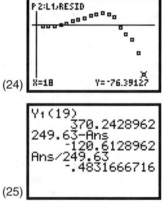

(20)

(21)

(22)

(23)

(24)

(25)

Topic 14—Logistic Fit

Note that the numbers of the steps below refer to the steps in Topic 11 that present more detail.

Step in Topic 11	Display	
1. *Calculate the fit equation.*	Press STAT <CALC> **B:Logistic L₁** ⬚ **ʟUSPOP** ⬚ **Y₁** for screen 26. Press ENTER, and notice the busy symbol in the upper-right corner of the display screen as calculations are being crunched out. The results are shown in screen 27. The technique used attempts to recursively estimate **a**, **b**, and **c** to make SSE as small as possible, and this takes some time.	(26)
		(27)
2. *Plot data scatter and fit equation.* 3. *Plot residuals.*	The logistic fit curve seems to snake through the data as seen in screen 28 and confirmed by the residual plot shown in screen 30.	(28)
	If after making the first plot (screen 28) you press ZOOM **3: Zoom Out** ENTER, you get the view that is shown in screen 29. The logistic curve levels off. It does not continue to grow as fast as the quadratic and exponential curves.	(29)
4. *Measure the fit (SSE).* 5. *Predict population in 1990 (X = 19).*	Screens 31 and 32 show SSE = **307.184**. The prediction for 1990 is 2.85 percent off the actual value.	(30)
		(31)
		(32)

Screen 26:
```
Logistic L₁,ʟUSP
OP,Y₁█
```

Screen 27:
```
Logistic
  y=c/(1+ae^(-bx))
  a=41.4518297
  b=.2298696561
  c=370.0016549
```

Screen 28:
```
P1:L1,USPOP
X=1              Y=7.24
```

Screen 29:
```
X=1.0361702  Y=7.8765613
```

Screen 30:
```
P2:L1,RESID
X=15            Y=-8.257338
```

Screen 31:
```
sum(ʟRESID²)
       307.1836453
```

Screen 32:
```
Y₁(19)
       242.5099505
249.63-Ans
         7.12004952
Ans/249.63
         .0285224112
```

Comparison of Fits Used (Topics 11 to 14)

The quadratic fit seemed best in the short run, but the logistic fit is not far behind and, hopefully, has the advantage of a more realistic long-run projection.

Fit	SSE	% Error X = 19	Resid Plot	Long Run
Linear	4652	17.1	clear pattern	grows linearly
Quadratic	131	0.4	seems random	grows prop to x^2
Exponential	9849	-48.3	clear pattern	grows exponentially
Logistic	307	2.9	screen 30	levels off

Topic 15—Median-Median Linear Fit

Xlist in **L1**: (horsepower)   75 80   85 100 125 135 160 175

Ylist in **L2**: (milles per gal.) 27 25   15   22   19   16   10   12

The data set above was selected to show the advantage of the median-median fit. Because the medians of batches of data are used, the fit is resistant to unusual data points.

Note that the numbers of the steps below refer to the steps in Topic 11 that present more detail.

Step in Topic 11	Display	
1. *Calculate the fit equation.*	Press STAT <CALC> **3:Med-Med L1 ⎵ L2 ⎵ Y1** for screen 33. Press ENTER for screen 34.	(33)
4. *Measure the fit (SSE).*	As shown in screen 35, SSE = **101.25**.	
2. *Plot data scatter and fit equation*	Press ZOOM **9:ZoomStat** TRACE ▶ ▶ for both a **Scatter** plot of the data (with point **x = 85** and **y = 15** highlighted) and of the **Med-Med** line, as shown in screen 36.	(34)
		(35)
		(36)

Screen (33):
```
Med-Med L₁,L₂,Y₁
■
```

Screen (34):
```
Med-Med
 y=ax+b
 a=-.1625
 b=38.26041667
```

Screen (35):
```
sum( LRESID²)
      101.2508681
```

Screen (36):
```
P1:L1,L2



     ☒

X=85          Y=15
```

Comparison with Least-Squares Fit Line

Note that the numbers of the steps below refer to the steps in Topic 11 that present more detail.

Step in Topic 11	Display

1. *Calculate the fit equation.*

    Press STAT <CALC>
    4:LinReg(ax + b) L1 , **L2** , **Y2**
    for screen 37 (be sure that you use **Y2** and not **Y1** as before). Press ENTER for screen 38. Note that **r** = -.823.

    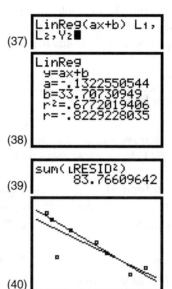

    (37)

    (38)

4. *Measure the fit (SSE).*

    As shown in screen 39, SSE = **83.77** is less than the **101.25** of **Med-Med** as theory guarantees. But having the smallest SSE does not always guarantee the better fit, as you can observe in the plots that follow in screen 40.

    (39)

2. *Plot data scatter and fit equation*

    With **Plot1**, **Y1**, and **Y2** on, press ZOOM **9:ZoomStat** for screen 40, which shows both the **Med-Med** and **LinReg** fit lines. Note that the least-squares line is pulled toward point **x** = 85, **y** = 15.

    (40)

If the point **x** = 85, **y** = 15 is deleted from **L1** and **L2** and a **LinReg** line plotted to the data, we obtain the results shown in screens 41 and 42. The slope and the intercept are about the same as the **Med-Med** fit without deleting the data point (see screen 34); **r** = -.976 compared to -.8229 in screen 38, and SSE = **11.74**, reduced from **83.77** in screen 39. The **Med-Med** fit is a good check on how influential such points are.

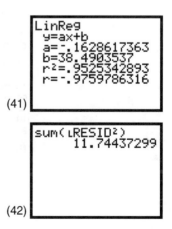

(41)

(42)

Topic 16—Trigonometric Sine Fit

Those who deal with periodic data, in Physics experiments, for example, will want to read about the **SinReg** (sinusoidal regression) function in the Statistics chapter of the *TI-83 Guidebook* for more information on this topic. The following data is from the example in the *Guidebook* with x representing the day of the year (equal intervals of every 30th day) and y the number of daylight hours in Alaska.

x (day) L1:	1	31	61	91	121	151	181	211	241	271	301	331	361
y (hrs) L2:	5.5	8	11	13.5	16.5	19	19.5	17	14.5	12.5	8.5	6.5	5.5

Note that the numbers of the steps below refer to the steps in Topic 11 that present more detail.

Step in Topic 11	Display
1. *Calculate the fit equation.*	Press STAT <**CALC**> **C:SinReg** L1 ⎵ L2 ⎵ **Y1** for screen 43. Press ENTER for screen 44.
2. *Plot data scatter and fit equation.*	Enter 2nd [STAT PLOT] <**Plot1**> with **Xlist: L1** and **Ylist: L2**. (**Y1** is on from step 1, but all other **Y=** or stat plots must be off.)
	Press ZOOM **9:ZoomStat** TRACE, and both a **Scatter** plot of the data and the sine fit will show as shown in screen 45.
	Press ZOOM **3: Zoom Out** ENTER to get the view shown in screen 46. This view better shows the periodic nature of the fit.

(43)
```
SinReg L1,L2,Y1■
```

(44)
```
SinReg
y=a*sin(bx+c)+d
a=6.770292445
b=.0162697853
c=-1.215498579
d=12.18138372
```

(45)

(46)

Activity 4

Describing Categorical Data

Topic 17 looks at the distribution of the population of the United States by the categorical variable race for one age group. Percentages are calculated, and visual comparison is made with a bar chart.

Topic 18 extends the discussion to a two-way table of race by age group. Age by itself is a quantitative variable, but ages are grouped into different categories (youngest, older, ...oldest) to have a manageable table. Percents and bar charts are compared.

Topic 17—Bar Charts

📖 *For this topic, set the mode for two decimal places. (Refer to "Setting Modes" under Do This First.)*

Population data, in thousands, for those under 15 years old follows.

Race:	White	Black	Asian Pacific Islander	Am. Indian Eskimo, Aleut
(thousands):	45510	8922	2243	664

(Source: Population by Age and Race 1994, Statistical Abstract of US 1995.)

1. Put the data in the spreadsheet in **L1, as shown in** screen 1.

2. With the fifth row highlighted, press [2nd] [LIST] **<MATH> 5:sum(L1**, as shown in the bottom line of screen 1.

(1)
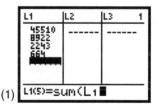

Activity 4, Describing Categorical Data (cont.)

3. Press ENTER for the first column of screen 2 with the sum of the first four rows showing in the fifth row.

4. Highlight **L2** as shown in screen 2, and type **L1** ÷ **L1** (**5**) × **100** in the bottom line.

   Press ENTER for the second column in screen 3, which lists the percent of those under 15 years old by race (**79.37**, **15.56**, **3.91**, and **1.16** for a total of **100** percent).

5. Enter **1**, **2**, **3**, **4**, and **9** in **L3**, as shown in screen 3.

To get a visual comparison of the difference in population for each race, you will construct a bar chart. This is easy to do by hand and not difficult with the TI-83. The **Histogram** plot of the TI-83 is used, so you might want to look at Topic 2.

Screen 4 sets up for a **Histogram** with the **Xlist** of **L3**, which contains the values 1, 2, 3, 4, and 9 for reasons explained in the next paragraph. The **Ylist** is **L2**, which contains the percent of each race.

Note that the **WINDOW** in screen 5 has **Xmax = 4.5** and **Xscl = 0.5**. The first bar starts with the first $x = 1$ and has a width of 0.5, so there is a gap between bars with the second bar starting at $x = 2$. The fifth value in **L2** has the total of 100 percent and $x = 9$ in **L3**, which is beyond **Xmax = 4.5**. Thus, a bar for the total will not be on the screen.

The bar chart in screen 6 clearly shows the large majority of whites in the population of those under 15 years old. Bar charts are often given in order of largest magnitude to smallest. The plot compares percents, but it has the exact proportions and shape of one that compares population counts. The percents add up to 100 percent. If population counts were used, they would add up to the total population.

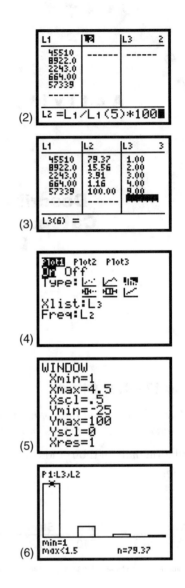

(2)

(3)

(4)

(5)

(6)

Topic 18—Two-Way Table

A more complete table of the data used in Topic 17 of the U.S. population of age by race, including more age groups, is given below. The population counts are in thousands.

Years:	White	Black	Asian Pacific Islander	Am. Indian Eskimo, Aleut
0 - 14	45510	8922	2243	664
15 - 29	44350	8020	2192	558
30 - 44	53045	7878	2400	512
45 - 59	35040	4190	1295	282
60 - 74	25405	2584	665	140
≥75	13120	1080	193	53

If you are only interested in a particular row or column of data, then put that data in **L1** and proceed as shown in Topic 17. If you wish to make many comparisons, then proceed as follows.

1. Set the mode to two decimals as shown in Do This First at the beginning of this handbook.

2. Put the four columns of data (of six rows each) in lists **L1** to **L4** (screen 7), and then calculate the column sums as follows.

    a. From the home screen, press [2nd] [LIST] **<MATH>** **5:sum(** L1 [STO▸] L1 [(] 7 [)]. This takes the sum of the values in **L1** (six values) and stores the sum in the seventh row of **L1**.

    b. Use [2nd] [ENTRY] and edit the list used to calculate the sum for each list, as shown in screen 7.

3. Use **L1** [+] **L2** [+] **L3** [+] **L4** [STO▸] **L5** [ENTER] to store the sum of each row (age group) in **L5**. (See screen 8.)

    The complete table of data, including the row and column totals, is shown in screens 9 and 10 and stored in lists **L1** to **L5**. You will also want to save this data in a matrix (see the next section).

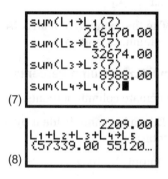

(7)

(8)

Note: *If your data source gave totals, you could have entered them. Because of rounding, they may have been a bit different from the totals obtained here.*

L1	L2	L3	1	L4	L5	4
45510	8922.0	2243.0		**664.00**	57339	
44350	8020.0	2192.0		558.00	55120	
53045	7878.0	2400.0		512.00	63835	
35040	4190.0	1295.0		282.00	40807	
25405	2584.0	665.00		140.00	28794	
13120	1080.0	193.00		53.00	14446	
216470	32674	8988.0		2209.0	260341	
L1(1)=45510				54		

(9)   (10)

Saving Data in Matrix [A]

To save the original count data, including totals, so you can make calculations that change the values in the spreadsheet, proceed as follows.

1. Press [2nd] [LIST] <OPS> 0:List▶matr(**L1** ☐ **L2** ☐ **L3** ☐ **L4** ☐ **L5** ☐ **[A]**, where **[A]** is pasted by pressing [MATRX] <NAMES> 1:[A] (see screen 11).

2. Press [ENTER] for **Done**, and then press [MATRX] <NAME> 1:[A] to paste **[A]** to the home screen, as shown in the last line of screen 11.

    After you paste **[A]** and press [ENTER], part of matrix **[A]** is revealed, as shown in screen 12.

3. Press the cursor control keys to reveal the rest of matrix **[A]**.

    The first column of matrix **[A]** is list **L1**, the second column, **L2**, and so on.

Calculating Column Percents

To calculate column percents, proceed as follows.

1. Take a list , and divide it by the seventh value (the total).

2. Multiply by 100.

3. Store the resulting percents to the same list.

    This procedure is done for **L1** to **L5** in screens 13 and 14. The results are revealed in the spreadsheet in screens 15 and 16.

4. Edit list **L6**, and a newly created list named **LC7** to contain values to draw comparative bar graphs.

    The results are shown in screen 17.

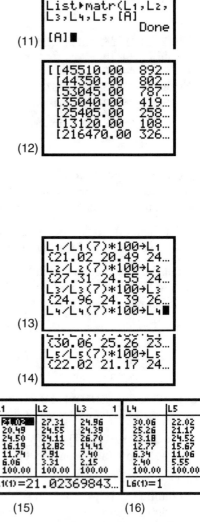

(11)

(12)

(13)

(14)

(15)   (16)

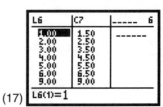

(17)

Drawing Comparative Bar Charts

Before starting here, it is a good idea to first read Topic 17 about single bar charts.

1. To get a visual comparison of the age distributions for two groups, white and black, set up the **WINDOW** and **Plot1** and **Plot2** for two **Histograms**, as shown in screens 18, 19, and 20.

2. Press TRACE for the bar charts, as shown in screen 21.

As you can see from the charts and from the previous table of column percents, a larger proportion of blacks are in the two youngest age groups than the proportion of whites in the same age groups. (The shading can be added by hand or in **Dot** mode with six commands: 2nd [DRAW] **7:Shade(0** , **L2** (**1**) ((**1.43 < X**) ((**X < 1.57**))), and then **7:Shade(0** , **L2** (**2**) ((**2.43 < X**) ((**X< 2.57**))), and so on; where < is pasted from 2nd [TEST] **5:<**.)

When making comparisons, do not confuse *percents* with *counts*. The fact that a larger percentage of blacks are in the youngest groups than the percentage of whites in the same groups does not mean that there are more blacks than whites in these groups.

Before you can continue making the comparative bar charts (described below), you must switch some data about as follows.

3. Save the column percents table in matrix **[C]** by pressing 2nd [LIST] <OPS> **0:List▸matr(L1** , **L2** , **L3** , **L4** , **L5** , **[C]** ENTER for **Done**. (See screen 22.)

4. Return the original data, with totals, in matrix **[A]** to the spreadsheet by pressing 2nd [LIST] <OPS> **A:Matr▸list([A]** , **L1** , **L2** , **L3** , **L4** , **L5** ENTER for **Done**. (See screen 22.)

To continue making the comparative bar charts:

5. Compare the counts for each age group with the original count data as shown in column **L1** and **L2**. The plots are set up the same as the previous bar charts of percents, but **Ymin** and **Ymax** have been adjusted to include all the counts (see screen 23).

6. Press TRACE, and add shading for the bar charts shown in screen 24.

You can see that there are many more whites than blacks in all age groups.

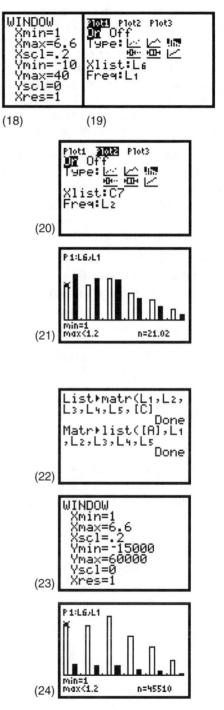

(18)   (19)

(20)

(21)

(22)

(23)

(24)

Activity 4, Describing Categorical Data (cont.)

Calculating the Percent of Each Cell

From the last value in **L5** in screen 10, you can see that the grand total of the population is **260,341** (thousand).

In the first age group (0 to 14 year olds), there are 45,510 (thousand) whites and 8,922 (thousand) blacks. This is about 17.5 percent of the whole population for whites in this age group, $100 * (45510/260341) = $ **45510 * (100/260341) = 17.48**, and about 3.4 percent for blacks in this age group, **8922 * (100/260341) = 3.43**. These calculations are shown in screen 25.

All the cells of the table (stored in **[A]**) can be multiplied by **100** and divided by **260,341**, as shown in screen 26. Note that the **17.48** percent and **3.43** percent you calculated above are in the first row of the resulting matrix (screen 27).

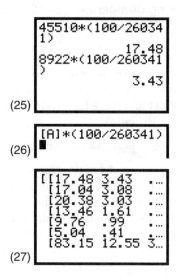

(25)

(26)

(27)

Calculating Row Percents

The example data for Topic 17 is really the first row of the two-way table. To calculate the percents with the data and totals in list **L1** to **L5**, proceed as follows.

1. Enter **L1** ⊠ **100** ÷ **L5** STO▸ **L1** ENTER for the first two lines in screen 28.

2. Press 2nd [ENTRY] to recall the last entry, press ◀ to move the flashing cursor over **L1**, and then change **L1** to **L2**.

3. Press ▲ to jump to the first **L1**, change this to **L2**, and then press ENTER for the third and fourth lines of screen 28.

4. Repeat the above steps for **L3**, **L4**, and **L5**, which are made up of the totals from the other rows, and thus all have values of 100 percent. (See the fourth line of screen 29.)

   You can observe the row percentages in **L1** to **L5** under STAT **1:Edit**.

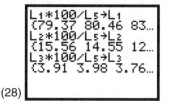

(28)

5. Store the results in matrix **[B]** as follows.

   a. Press [2nd] [LIST] **<OPS> 0:List▸matr(L₁** [,] **L₂** [,] **L₃**
      [,] **L₄** [,] **L₅** [,] **[B]**, where **[B]** is pasted by pressing
      [MATRX] **<NAMES> 2:[B]** (see screen 29).

   b. Press [ENTER] for **Done**, and then press [MATRX]
      <NAMES>2:[B] to paste **[B]** to the home screen, as
      shown in the last line of screen 29.

   After you paste **[B]** and press [ENTER], part of matrix [B]
   is revealed, as shown in screen 30.

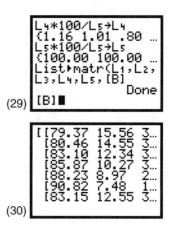

(29)

6. Press the cursor control keys to reveal the rest of
   matrix **[B]**.

   The values in the first row (**79.37**, **15.56**, **3.91**, and **1.16**
   percent) are the same as shown in Topic 17.

(30)

Making Bar Charts for Rows

If you want the rows of percents to be set up in lists to
construct bar charts with the TI–83, one solution is to store the
transpose of matrix **[B]** in matrix **[E]** with the original rows of
[B] now columns in **[E]**.

1. First, paste **[B]** to the home screen, and then press
   [MATRX] **<MATH> 2:ᵀ** [STO▸] **[E]** for the first line in screen
   31.

2. Press [ENTER] for matrix **[E]**, part of which is shown in
   screen 31.

   The first row of **[B]** represents the youngest age groups'
   percents now located in the first column of **[E]**.

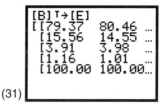

(31)

3. Transfer these lists from **[E]** to the spreadsheet, and
   plot bar charts as shown previously in this topic.

Activity 5

Collecting Data

Topic 19 shows how to use random numbers to collect samples (from which data is obtained) and how to randomly assign subjects to experiments to collect data.

Topic 20 gives an example of how the TI-83, along with the Calculator Based Laboratory™ (CBL™) System, can be used to collect data dynamically (in real time).

Topic 19—Random Sampling and Randomization for Experiments

The following table represents a class of 24 students with 15 females and 9 males.

1 *	2	3	4 *	5	6
Bertha	Joe	Kay	Flora	Kojo	Bernice
F1	M1	F2	F3	M2	F4
7 *	8	9	10	10	12
Marge	Barbara	Jim	Narissa	Walter	Shaine
F5	F6	M3	F7	M4	F8
13 *	14	15 *	16	17	18 *
Ann	Frank	Chris	Esi	Shirley	Cheyenne
F9	M5	M6	F10	F11	F12
19 *	20	21	22	23	24 *
Tom	Pete	Ruby	Max	Linda	Mary
M7	M8	F13	M9	F14	F15

Random Sampling

Simple Random Samples

1. To select a committee of eight students with each student having an equal chance of being selected, give the student an identification number (use the numbers 1 to 24 above the students' names in the table).

2. Set a seed for the random-number generator. (This is done so you can duplicate the results in this handbook. If that is not important to you, then there is no need to set the seed.)

   If you wish your seed to be different from others, the last four digits of your Social Security Number should work.

3. Type **456** [STO▶] [MATH] [◀] **<PRB> 1:rand** [ENTER] for the first two lines in screen 1.

4. Press [MATH] [◀] **<PRB> 5:randInt(1** [,] 24 [,] 5 [ENTER] [ENTER] for the next three lines in screen 1.

   The randomly generated integers, which all have values between 1 and 24 with possible repeats, are grouped by five because this number is convenient and shows well on the screen.

   The first eight integers, after ignoring the repeated 24, are **24, 7, 19, 4, 18, 13, 15, 1**, or in order: **1, 4, 7, 13, 15, 18, 19, 24**. The committee is made up of Bertha, Flora, Marge, Ann, Chris, Cheyenne, Tom, and Mary, thus six females and two males. If these people stood up in an actual classroom, you could see how they are scattered about the room with different heights, weights, and gender (see the asterisks next to the identification numbers in the class table to see some of this variability).

(1)

```
456→rand
               456
randInt(1,24,5
   {24 7 19 24 4}
   {18 13 15 1 17}
```

Stratified Sampling

In the previous example, if you want to ensure that the committee is made up in the same proportion of males and females that are in the class, you would need five females and three males (15/24 = 5/8 and 9/24 = 3/8). Do this as follows.

1. Number the female class members F1 to F15 and the male class members M1 to M9 (see the numbers under the names in the class table).

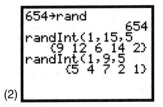

(2)

2. Set the seed, and generate random integers from 1 to 15 and from 1 to 9, as shown in screen 2, for the following committee (in order).

   Female: F2, F6, F9, F12, F14, or Kay, Bernice, Ann, Cheyenne, and Linda.

   Male: M4, M5, M7, or Walter, Frank, and Tom.

Randomization in Experimental Designs

Randomization is an important component of conducting an experiment. The example that follows tests two teaching methods in our class of 24 students. You will assign the first 12 randomly selected students to Method I with the remainder assigned to Method II.

(3)

1. Set the seed and generate random integers between 1 and 24, as shown in screen 3.

   The first 12 values (ignoring repeats of 6 and 20) are **6, 8, 20, 1, 5, 17, 9, 14, 18, 12, 19**, and **24**. In order they are **1, 5, 6, 8, 9, 12, 14, 17, 18, 19, 20, 24**.

   As a result, Bertha, Kojo, Bernice, Bernie, Jim, Shaine, Frank, Shirley, Cheyenne, Tom, Pete, and Mary are assigned to Method I. The remaining 12 students are assigned to Method II.

Topic 20—Gathering Data with the CBL

The CBL System from Texas Instruments comes with a
workbook that has detailed instructions and listings of the
programs necessary to do many experiments. Texas
Instruments has other manuals with activities for the CBL.
Real-World Math with the CBL System by Brueningsen et al
has activities that could be adopted to hypotheses testing. For
example, in Activity 15 of the Brueningsen book, you could
hypothesize that the dominant hand can generate more rapid
light pulses than the non-dominant hand; or in Activity 22, you
could test if one group (for example, basketball players) jumps
higher, on average, than another (non-basketball players or
football players).

The experiment below is modified from the *CBL SYSTEM
Experiment Workbook* and uses the temperature probe that
comes with the CBL unit. This experiment was picked because
it is easy to set up and conduct.

Newton's Law of Cooling

The rate at which a warm body cools is proportional to the
temperature difference between the temperature of the warm
object (T) and the temperature of its surroundings (C).
Mathematically, this is equivalent to $(T - C) = A * e^{-kt}$, where A
is a constant depending on the initial temperature of the object
and k is a proportionality constant. (See "Experiment P3" in the
CBL SYSTEM Experiment Workbook.) This experiment works
well with Topic 13 and with model fitting.

A hot cup of coffee cools because the surrounding air is at a
lower temperature. The greater the temperature difference, the
more rapid the cooling. As the coffee approaches room
temperature, it cools very slowly and remains lukewarm for a
long period. We say its temperature is lowering at a decreasing
rate instead of at the constant rate a straight line would
indicate on a plot of temperature versus time. To show the
relationship between temperature and time, do the following.

1. Put some boiling water in a Thermos™ for easy and safe
    transport.

2. Connect the TI-83 to the CBL as if it were another
    TI-83. Connect the temperature probe to **CH2** on the top
    edge of the CBL unit.

3.   Turn on both the CBL unit and the TI-83.

---

4. With the temperature probe at room temperature, run the **COOLTEMP** program from the workbook (and listed at the end of this topic).

   To avoid conduction and evaporation effects on the temperature probe, do not place the probe directly on the table top or expose it to any drafts.

5. After the **COOLTEMP** program has run about 30 seconds, put the probe into the hot water, and watch the temperature rise. (See screen 4.)

6. After the **COOLTEMP** program stops running (about 1.5 minutes), press TRACE, and read the room temperature (26.07°C), the **Y** value shown in the bottom of screen 4.

7. Lift the probe from the water, flick off the last drop of water, and run the **COOLTEMP** program for the cooling curve in screen 5. (Again, keep the probe out of drafts, and do not let it touch the table.)

   Notice how the probe cooled a bit before you started recording and how the temperature continues to drop, leveling off to the room temperature.

8. Because the rate of change of the temperature is proportional to the difference between the temperature of the liquid and the room temperature, subtract room temperature from each of the liquid readings stored by the program in **L4**. Note that the time, in seconds, is stored in **L2**.

   a. From the home screen, enter **L4** − **26.07** STO▸ **L4**.

   b. Press GRAPH for screen 6. With the room temperature subtracted, this curve is approaching zero as you might expect.

   c. Press ZOOM **9:ZoomStat**, and the data fills up the screen, as shown in screen 7.

9. The line is not straight. Theory predicts exponential cooling, so do as follows.

   a. Press STAT [CALC] **0:ExpReg L2, L4, Y1** ENTER, which gives screen 8 with **y = a ∗ bˣ**, where **a = 34.37582181** and **b = 0.9700960904**.

   b. Press GRAPH for screen 9, which shows this curve fitting the data very well.

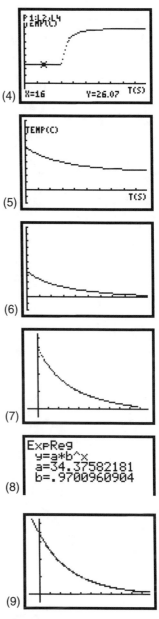

(4)

(5)

(6)

(7)

(8)

(9)

Note: 34.3758 ∗ 0.9701ˣ =
34.3758 ∗ e^(ln0.9701 ∗ X) =
34.3758 ∗ e^(-0.0304 ∗ X).

Program COOLTEMP.83p

```
PlotsOff
Func
FnOff
AxesOn
0→Xmin
99→Xmax
10→Xscl
-20→Ymin
100→Ymax
10→Yscl
ClrList L2,L4
ClrHome
{1,0}→L1
Send(L1)
{1,2,1}→L1
Send(L1)
99→dim(L4)
ClrHome
Disp "PRESS ENTER TO"
Disp "START GRAPHING"
Disp "TEMPERATURE:"
Pause
ClrDraw
Text(4,1,"TEMP(C)":Text(54,81,"T(S)")
{3,1,-1,0}→L1
Send(L1)
For(I,1,99,1)
Get(L4(I))
Pt-On(I,L4(I))
End
seq(N,N,0,98,1)→L2
0→Xmin
max(L2)→Xmax
10→Xscl
Plot1(Scatter,L2,L4,·)
DispGraph
Text(4,1,"TEMP(C)"):Text(54,81,"T(S)")
Stop
```

EXPLORATIONS

Activity 6

Demonstrating Probability, Simulations, and Probability Distributions

This activity demonstrates the probability of an event happening with the simple example of simulating the tossing of a coin.

📖 It is important that you understand the concept of "random seed" described in Topic 21 to fully understand all other topics that contain simulations.

Other topics explain how probabilities can be calculated or give a simulation that shows the reasonableness of the results found. Topics 29 and 30 may be of interest to those who seek ideas on using simulations to solve probability problems.

Topic 21—Coin Toss (The Law of Large Numbers)

If you toss four coins, you might get all tails, but in the long run, you would expect about half heads (.50) and half tails.

Setting a Random Seed

To simulate tossing of coins, you will set a random seed so that the results can be duplicated. If you have no need to duplicate these results, then skip this step. If you want to assure that your results are different from others, you can use the last four digits of your Social Security Number as your seed.

1. Type **321** [STO▸] [MATH] **<PRB> 1:rand** [ENTER], as shown in the first two lines in screen 1.

2. Put the numbers 1 to 150 in **L₁** using [2nd] [LIST] **<OPS> 5:seq(X** [,] **X** [,] **1** [,] **150** [STO▸] **L₁** [ENTER].

3. Generate one (1) random coin toss at a time with a 0.5 chance of getting a head = H = 1. Do this 150 times.

    Store the results in **L₂** with [MATH] **<PRB> 7:randBin(1** [,] **.5** [,] **150** [STO▸] **L₂** [ENTER].

The results {**1 0 1 0 1 1 0** ... shown in screen 2 can be read as {H T H T H H T...

(1)

(2)

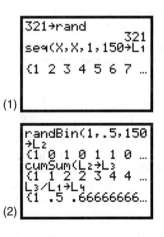

4. Press [2nd] [LIST] <OPS> 6:cumSum(L2 [STO▸] L3 to store
    the cumulative sum of L2 in L3. The results {1 1 2 2 3 4 4
    ... indicate that the first head occurred on the first toss
    (1), the second head on the third toss (1 + 0 + 1= 2), the
    third head at the fifth toss (1 + 0 + 1 + 0 + 1 = 3), and so
    on (see screen 2).

5. Press L3 [÷] L1 [STO▸] L4 to get the proportion of heads.

    {1 .5 .6666... indicates 100 percent (1/1 = 1) heads on the
    first toss; 50 percent (1/2) heads after the second toss,
    because there is still just one head; and 66.67 percent
    heads, or two out of three heads, after the third toss.
    (See the last line of screen 2.)

In the short run, this is a lot of fluctuation.

To see what happens in the long run, set up and plot the results
as follows.

1. Press [2nd] [STAT PLOT] **1:Plot1** to set up for an **xyLine**
    plot, as shown in Topic 9 (see screen 3).

2. Press [Y=] and set **Y**1 **= 0.5** to plot this horizontal line
    (see screen 4).

3. Set the **WINDOW** as shown in screen 5, and then press
    [TRACE] for the plot of the first ten tosses (**Xmax = 10**) as
    shown in screen 6.

4. Using [WINDOW], change **Xmax** to 100, leaving the other
    values as shown in screen 5.

5. Press [TRACE] for the plot in screen 7, which covers 100
    tosses.

    The first tic mark on the x-axis marks off the first 10
    tosses, and the plot to that point is the same as shown
    in screen 6 but condensed by the change of scale.
    Notice how the plotted points hover about the **Y**1 **= 0.5**
    line.

6. Press [STAT] **1:Edit**, and use [▾] to move to the tenth row
    of proportions in L4 with **0.4** (see screen 8).

    L3 has the number of heads, or four out of ten. You can
    investigate this from the home screen with L3 [(] 10 [)],
    as shown in screen 9. Screen 9 also shows that after 100
    tosses, there are 55 heads and 45 tails (so the
    proportion of heads is 55/100 = 0.55), and the 150th toss
    gives 76 heads and 74 tails (76/150 = 0.506667).

In the long run, the proportion of heads is approximately 0.5.

(3)

(4)

(5)

(6)

(7)

(8)

(9)

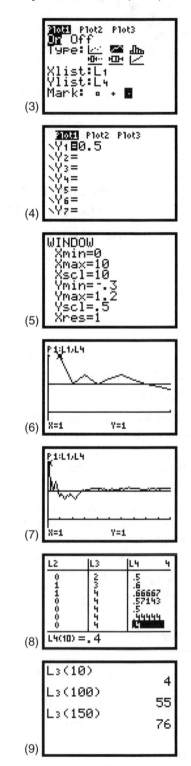

Topic 22—Factorials, Permutations, and Combinations

The following functions have many uses, including calculating probabilities, as you will see in later topics.

Using Factorials

A. How many ways can you pick a president and vice-president from two people, Ann and James?

There are two choices for president, Ann and James. For each of these choices, there is only one choice left for vice-president. Therefore, $2 * 1 = 2! = 2$ ways: Ann James and James Ann.

Press 2 $\boxed{\text{MATH}}$ **<PRB>4:!** $\boxed{\text{ENTER}}$ for **2**, as shown in screen 10.

B. How many ways can you set up a slate of 10 people for 10 positions?

$10 * 9 * 8 * 7 * 6 * 5 * 4 * 3 * 2 * 1 = 3{,}628{,}800$ possible slates.

(10)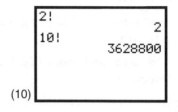

Using Permutations

How many ways can you pick a slate of two (president and vice-president) from four (Ann, James, Carl, and Doris)?

There are four choices for president. For each of these four choices, there are three choices for vice-president for a total of $4 * 3 = (4 * 3 * 2 * 1)/(2 * 1) = 4!/2! = 12$ possible slates:

Ann James	James Ann	Carl Ann	Doris Ann
Ann Carl	James Carl	Carl James	Doris James
Ann Doris	James Doris	Carl Doris	Doris Carl

Press 4 $\boxed{\text{MATH}}$ **<PRB> 2:nPr 2** $\boxed{\text{ENTER}}$ for **12**, as in screen 11.

(11)

Using Combinations

How many ways can you make a committee of two from the four people above?

Because order is not important in setting up a committee (Ann James is a different slate than James Ann, but they make up the same committee); in fact, there are 2! too many values above. Therefore, $4!/(2!2!) = 6$ ways: Ann James, Ann Carl, Ann Doris, James Carl, James Doris, and Carl Doris.

Press 4 $\boxed{\text{MATH}}$ **<PRB>3:nCr 2** $\boxed{\text{ENTER}}$ for **6**, as shown in screen 11.

Topic 23—Binomial Distribution

The production of an electronic component has a large 20 percent defective rate. If a random selection of six components is taken,

A. What is the probability of getting exactly two defectives?

B. What is the probability of getting at most two defectives?

C. What is the probability of getting at least two defectives?

D. What is the probability of getting from two to four defectives?

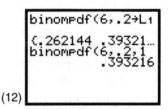

(12)

Note: pdf stands for probability density function.

Generate the complete distribution by pressing 2nd [DISTR] **0:binompdf(6** [,] [.] **2** STO▸ **L1** ENTER for the first two lines of screen 12, and then pressing STAT **1:Edit** to reveal the probabilities in **L1**. The values of 0 to 6 have been keyed into **L2**, as shown in screen 13.

A. $P(1) = $ **.39322** is in the second row of the spreadsheet under **L1** (see screen 13), but you can calculate it directly using 2nd [DISTR] **0:binompdf(6** [,] [.] **2** [,] **1** ENTER for the results shown in the last two lines of screen 12.

B. $P(0) + P(1) + P(2) = $ **.90112** is the sum of the first three values of **L1**, but you can also calculate it directly using 2nd [DISTR] **A:binomcdf(6** [,] [.] **2** [,] **2** ENTER for the results shown in the first two lines of screen 14. (The remainder of the screen shows an alternate method.)

C. $P(2) + P(3) + P(4) + P(5) + P(6) = 1 - (P(0) + P(1)) = $ **.34464**, or 1 [−] 2nd [DISTR] **A:binomcdf(6** [,] [.] **2** [,] **1** ENTER for the results shown in screen 15.

D. $P(2) + P(3) + P(4) = $ **0.34304** $= (P(0) + (P(1) + P(2) + P(3) + P(4))-(P(0) + P(1))$, or 2nd [DISTR] **A:binomcdf(6** [,] [.] **2** [,] **4** [)] [−] 2nd [DISTR] **A:binomcdf(6** [,] [.] **2** [,] **1** [)] ENTER as shown in screen 16. (Note that **sum(binompdf(6** [,] [.] **2** [,] **{2** [,] **3** [,] **4 }** [)] also gives the same results.)

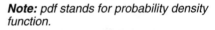

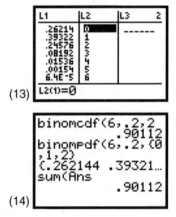

(13)

(14)

Note: cdf stands for cumulative density function.

(15)

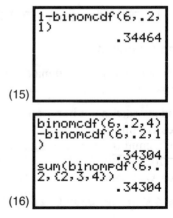

(16)

Constructing a Probability Histogram

1. Set up **Plot1** and the **WINDOW** as shown in screens 17 and 18 and as discussed in Topic 2 on **Histogram**s.

2. Press TRACE for the probability **Histogram** in screen 19 with $P(0) = $ **n = 0.262144**.

Displaying Mean and Standard Deviation

With X in **L2** and probabilities in **L1**, pressing STAT **<CALC>** **1:1-Var Stats L2** ⸳ **L1** displays screen 20, and then pressing ENTER gives screen 21.

Note that $\mu = \bar{x} = $ **1.2** $= n * p = 6 * 0.2 = 1.2$ and $\sigma = \sigma x = $ **0.9797958971** $= \sqrt{(n * p(1 - p))} = \sqrt{(6 * 0.2 * 0.8)}$.

Large Sample Domain Errors

If the sample size is too large (≥ 1000), a domain error will occur, as demonstrated in screens 22 and 23 (**n** = 999 works fine, but **n** = 1000 gives an error). You can approximate many large sample binomial distribution problems by using the *normal distribution* as explained at the end of Topic 24.

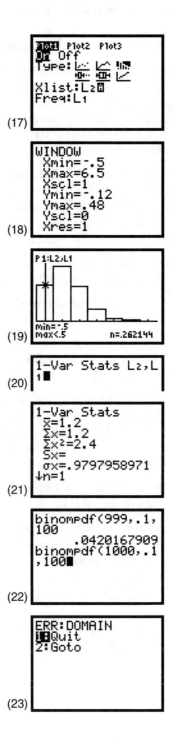

(17)

(18)

(19)

(20)

(21)

(22)

(23)

Topic 24—Normal Distribution

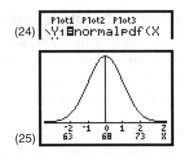

(24)

Assume you are given a normal population of heights with $\mu = 68$ inches and $\sigma = 2.5$ inches. You can plot the normal probability density function (screen 25) with a **WINDOW**, as shown in screens 26, by pressing Y=, and then with the cursor after **Y₁=**, pressing 2nd [DISTR] **1:normalpdf(X** (see screen 24) and then GRAPH.

(25)

Note: The z values -2, -1, 0, 1, 2, and some of the corresponding heights of 63, 68, and 73 inches have been added to the plot.

A. What proportion of the population is between 65.5 and 70.5 inches tall or between the z values of -1 and 1? This also could be stated as, what is the probability that a person picked at random from the population has a height between 65.5 and 70.5 inches?

1. Press 2nd [DISTR] **2:normalcdf(-1** , **1** ENTER for **.6827**, as shown in the first two lines in screen 27.

2. Enter the heights directly or shade an area for the answer.

   To enter the heights directly, add μ and σ, as shown in screen 27, using 2nd [DISTR] **2:normalcdf(65** . **5** . **70** . **5** . **68** . **2** . **5** ENTER for **0.6827**.

   To shade an area for the answer, with the **WINDOW** as given in screen 26 and with all plots off, press 2nd [DISTR] <DRAW> **1:ShadeNorm(** – **1** , **1** ENTER for the shaded plot, as shown in screen 29, where **Area = .6827** is given below the plot.

B. What proportion of the population is greater than 73 inches or a z value greater than 2?

1. Press 2nd [DISTR] **2:normalcdf(2** , **E99** ENTER (obtain the **E** by pressing 2nd [EE] above .) for **.02275** with **E99 = 10⁹⁹**, a very large number or "infinity."

   Note that the original height (73 inches) could have been used, as shown in screen 30, if we had used **normalcdf(73** , **E99** , **68** , **2** . **5** ENTER for **0.02275**.

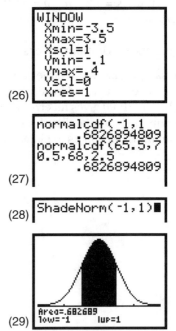

(26)

(27)

(28)

(29)

Note: It may be necessary to clear a previous plot as in step 2.

(30)

---

2. To shade the desired area after working problem A,

   (a) Clear the previous drawing or shading using [2nd] [DRAW] **1:ClrDraw** [ENTER] for **Done** on the home screen, as shown in screen 31.

   (b) Press [2nd] [DISTR] **<DRAW> 1:ShadeNorm(2 [,] E99 [)] [ENTER]** for the shaded graph in screen 32.

C. What proportion of the population is less than 73 inches tall?

From problem B, this would be 1 - 0.02275 = 0.97725, but you can also do this as shown in screens 33, 34, and 35 with negative infinity given as -**E99**.

Finding a Value From a Given Proportion

D. What height separated the tallest 5 percent of the population from the other 95 percent?

Press [2nd] [DISTR] **3:invNorm(0 [.] 95 [ENTER]** for a z value of **1.645**. From this value, you can calculate the height as $\mu + z\sigma$, or $68 + 1.645 * 2.5 = $ **72.112**. (See screen 36.)

The height itself is returned if you add μ and σ using [2nd] [DISTR] **3:invNorm(0 [.] 95 [,] 68 [,] 2 [.] 5 [ENTER]** for **72.112** inches. (See the last lines of screen 36.)

Using Normal Approximation to the Binomial

At the end of Topic 23, you saw that **n** = 999 was the largest sample size that the binomial functions could handle. If **n** is larger than 999, the following method (which is justified in Topic 25) can be used if $n * p \geq 10$ (some texts say 5) and $n * (1 - p) \geq 10$. If **n** = 999 and $p = 0.1$, you have $999 * 0.1 = 99.9$ and $999 * 0.9 = 899.1$, which are both ≥ 10.

We will use **n** = 999 and $p = 0.1$ to show how well the method works.

Use a normal distribution with $\mu = n * p = 99.9$ and $\sigma = \sqrt{(n * p * (1 - p))} = \sqrt{(999 * 0.1 * 0.9)} = $ **9.482**. (See screen 37.)

(31)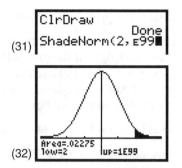

(32)

Note: *ShadeNorm(73,E99,68,2.5 also works but the window must be adjusted accordingly for each change in μ or σ while the window in screen 26 works for all standard normal distributions or z values.*

(33)

(34)

(35)

(36)

(37)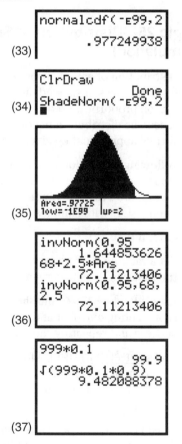

A. What is the probability of exactly 100 successes?

    The discrete binomial **Histogram** has a rectangle of base 1 and the height of the probability. For $X = 100$, the base goes from 99.5 to 100.5 with area under the normal curve of **0.0421** compared to the exact binomial answer of **0.0420**. (See screen 38.)

    (38)

B. What is the probability of less then 100 successes?

    Normal approx. = **0.483**. Exact binomial = **0.489**. (See screen 39.)

    (39)

C. What is the probability of from 100 to 200 successes?

    Normal approx. = **0.517**. Exact binomial = **0.511**. (See screen 40.)

    (40)

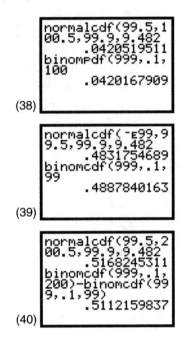

Topic 25—Distribution of Sample Proportions (Simulation)

The distribution of sample proportions will be simulated. For small sample sizes, a skewed distribution results because the population proportion used is not 0.5. As the sample size increases, the distribution becomes more normal, reinforcing the normal approximating given at the end of Topic 23.

The following simulation is of a sampling from a very large population with 67 percent whites and 33 percent other races. (Topic 47 shows that the binomial simulator **randBin** works very well.) Start with samples of size 10.

p = 0.67, n = 10

1. Set a random seed as explained in Topic 21 and given in the first two lines in screen 41.

    (41)

2. Press MATH <PRB>7:randBin(1 ⎡.⎤ 0 ⎡.⎤ 67 ⎡.⎤ 10 representing *one* pick at a time with a *0.67* chance of a success and repeating the selection *ten* times.

3. Press ENTER ENTER ENTER for the three sets of 0s and 1s, as shown in screens 42, 43, and 44 (your screen will not give the complete list, but using ▶ will reveal the last values).

    (42)

    (43)

    (44)

    One (**1**) represents a "white," thus with 67 percent, or approximately 70 percent whites, you would expect *about* seven **1**s and three **0**s. The first three samples reveal six, seven, and nine **1**s, respectively, out of 10, or 0.6, 0.7, and 0.9 proportion of successes.

4. Reset the seed, and calculate the sum of ten values generated at a time from the population with $p = 0.67$ for 100 samples.

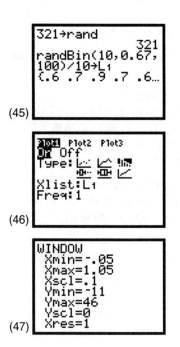

(45)

Divide each sum by 10 for the proportion of success in each sample, and store in **L₁**. (See screen 45.)

Notice in screen 45 that the first three values of **.6, .7,** and **.9** are from the first three samples above with sums of 6, 7, and 10.

5. Set up **Plot1** for a **Histogram** as shown in screen 46, and set the **WINDOW** as shown in screen 47.

(46)

6. Press TRACE, and use ▶ to highlight the class with the largest frequency (26), which is also the class that contains the value of 0.67, as shown in screen 48.

The distribution is somewhat skewed to the left because with $p = 0.67$, we would not expect many samples to have no whites or even only one or two whites. The frequency distribution from the previous **Histogram** is given in the following table.

(47)

p:	0	0.1	0.2	0.3	0.4	0.5	0.6	0.7	0.8	0.9	1
Frequency:	0	0	0	2	3	12	23	26	24	10	0

The measure of the spread for a binomial distribution is $\sigma = \sqrt{(p(1 - p)/n)} = \sqrt{(0.67 *.33/10)} = .1487 = 0.15$, as shown in the first two lines in screen 49.

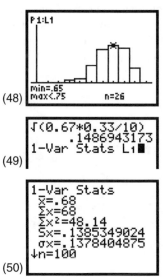

(48)

7. Press STAT <CALC> 1:1-Var Stats L₁ ENTER.

This gives **Sx = .1385 = 0.14** (screen 50) from the simulation, which is approximately the same as above. The mean of **0.68** is close to the theoretical value of 0.67.

(49)

(50)

p = 0.67, n = 30

Repeat the steps on the previous page with a larger sample size of **n** = 30.

The distribution becomes more symmetric and more closely centered on p = **0.67**. Note that the first sample gives $(6 + 7 + 9)/30 = $ **.73333333**. (See screen 51.) Recall that 6, 7, and 9 were the totals for the first three batches of ten values simulated. (See screen 45.)

As you can see in screen 52, as the sample size increases, the distribution of sample proportions is squeezing more closely to the population value of p = 0.67.

Sx = .0831 = 0.083 is very close to σ = **.0858 = 0.086**. The mean of **0.679** is close to the theoretical value of 0.670. (See the calculations in screens 53 and 54.)

Because the mean of the sample proportions is the same as the population proportion, the sample proportion is said to be an *unbiased estimator* of the population proportion. (See Topic 39.)

The property of getting a more normal-like distribution with a smaller standard deviation as sample size increases can be proven by the *Central Limit Theorem*. The *Central Limit Theorem* is usually discussed in terms of sample means (see Topic 26). If you consider a success a "1" and a failure a "0," then a proportion is indeed a mean.

Note: *It may be helpful for a class of students to first do the simulation on the previous page by tossing dice. Have each student toss a die ten times and record the number showing, for example, (6, 2, 3, 4, 3, 2, 5, 4, 6, 6). Count the number of times 3, 4, 5, or 6 appears (eight times in our example or a proportion of 0.80). If 25 students do this one time (or four times) each, store the 25 (or 100) proportions in* **L1**, *construct a* **Histogram**, *and then calculate the* **1-Var Stats**. *The results obtained will be similar to that above because* $p = 4/6 = 0.666... = 0.67.$

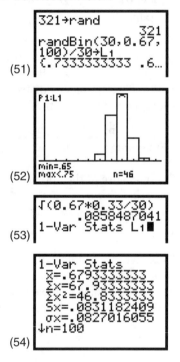

(51)

(52)

(53)

(54)

Topic 26—Distribution of Sample Means (Central Limit Theorem) (Simulation)

📖 *For this topic, set the mode for two decimal places. (Refer to "Setting Modes" under Do This First.)*

The distribution of sample means will be simulated from a continuous uniform distribution with all possible values between 0 and 10 (see screen 55). This population has $\mu = 5.00$ and $\sigma = 2.89$.

As sample sizes from the above population increases, you will see that the distribution of the means of these samples becomes more normally distributed with $\mu = 5.00$ and $\sigma = 2.89/\sqrt{(n)}$.

Sample Size n = 1

1. Set a random seed as explained in Topic 21 and shown in the first two lines in screen 56.

2. Type **10** [MATH] **<PRB>1:rand** [( ] **100** [ )] [STO▸] **L₁** [ENTER].

   This gives a set of 100 random values between 0 and 10, starting with **3.25, 7.44, 3.41, 6.23, 4.28...4.13, 2.70**, as shown in the last line of screen 56. (Use [▸] to see the rest of the values.)

3. Set up **Plot1** for a **Histogram** (screen 57), and set up the **WINDOW** as shown in screen 58.

4. Press [TRACE] for the **Histogram** of the 100 values, as shown in screen 59.

   Because there are ten classes, you would expect about ten values per class.

5. Press [STAT] **<CALC> 1:1-Var Stats L₁** [ENTER].

   This gives **Sx = 2.74**, or approximately the same as $\sigma = $ **2.89, or 2.89/$\sqrt{(1)}$**. The mean of **4.88** is approximately the same as the theoretical value for all possible samples $\mu = 5.00$. (See screens 60 and 61.)

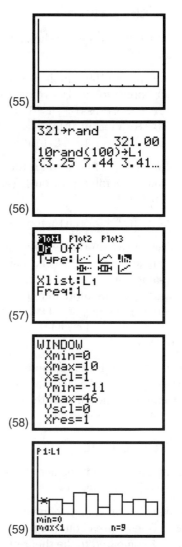

(55)

(56)

(57)

(58)

(59)

Note: *There are 9 values in the first class with 10, 7,15, 14, 5, 14, 8, 10, and 8 in the other classes. Topic 47 shows that these results are reasonable.*

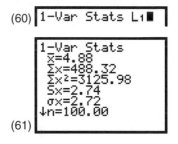

(60)

(61)

Sample Size n = 5

1. Set a random seed as shown in the first two lines in screen 62.

2. To generate 100 sample means of samples of size 5 from our population and store the results in **L1** (as shown in screen 62), press 2nd [LIST] <OPS> 5:seq(2nd [LIST] <MATH> 3:mean(10 MATH <PRB> 1:rand (5)) , X , 1 , 100) STO▸ **L1** ENTER.

    Note that the first mean is the mean of the first five values generated previously $(3.25 + 7.44 + 3.41 + 6.23 + 4.28)/5 = 4.92$.

3. Press TRACE for the **Histogram** shown in screen 63.

    Previously, nine values were in the first class, but now there are none. (It is very unlikely that all five values in a sample would be so small that their mean is less than 1. Samples are more like the one in the paragraph above. For every small value like 3.25, there is probably a larger value like 7.44 that brings the average closer to $\mu = 5.00$.)

The mean of all the 100 samples is **4.85**, not too far from the theoretical value of 5.00 for all possible samples. **Sx = 1.20** is approximately the same as the theoretical value of **2.89/√(5) = 1.29**. (See screens 64 and 65.)

Sample Size n = 10

Repeat as above, but replace the 5 with 10. (The 2nd [ENTRY] feature is helpful here.)

The distribution is more centered around $\mu = 5.0$ with a mean of **4.96**. It is less spread out than the smaller samples above with **Sx= 0.87** compared to the theoretical value for all possible samples of size 10 of $2.89/\sqrt{(10)} = 0.91$. (See screens 66-69.)

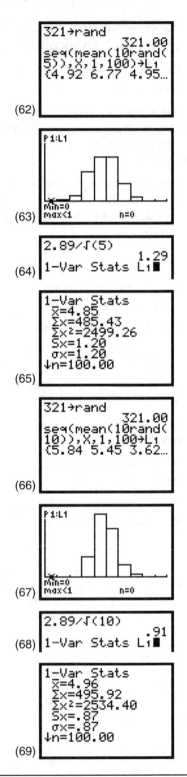

(62)

(63)

(64)

(65)

(66)

(67)

(68)

(69)

Central Limit Theorem

As sample sizes from a population increase, the distribution of the means of these samples becomes more normally distributed with the mean of all possible samples the same as the population mean μ. (The sample mean is an unbiased estimator of the population mean. See Topic 39.) The standard deviation for all possible samples, the population standard deviation, is divided by the square root of the sample size $(\sigma /\sqrt{(n)}$. (For a check on the normality of our samples, see Topic 27.)

Topic 27—Assessing Normality (Normal Probability Plots)

📖 *For screens 70-78 in this topic, set the mode for two decimal places; for screens 79-85, return the mode to floating decimal. (Refer to "Setting Modes" under Do This First.)*

A **Histogram** or a stem-and-leaf plot can give an indication if a group of data is normally distributed or not. A normal probability plot is better for assessing normality in that the eye can more easily check if the data points lie on a straight line.

Working with Sample Means

In Topic 26, 100 sample means were generated by generating samples of size 10 with a uniform random-number generator. A **Histogram** was constructed from the sample means (screens 66 and 67). This **Histogram** is duplicated in screens 70 and 71.

To plot a normal probability plot, turn on **Plot1** as shown in screen 72, and then press ZOOM **9:ZoomStat** TRACE.

The plot constructed (see screen 73) gives good evidence of normality because the line is fairly straight and the points are more dense in the center while thinning out in the tails.

Note: *It may be helpful with a class of students to first do a simulation by tossing a die. Although these will be discrete rather than continuous distributions, the idea is still clear. For example, if a student tosses a die 10 times for the following results grouped into two sets of five values: [(6,2,3,4,3), (2,5,4,6,6)], there are no 1s, two 2s, two 3s, two 4s, one 5, and three 6s. These can be combined with other class members' results for a fairly uniform distribution of 1s, 2s, 3s, 4s, 5s, and 6s with a mean of 3.5 and a standard deviation of approximately 1.71.*

*If you calculate the average of the two groups of five digits, you obtain, in our example, (6 + 2 + 3 + 4 +3)/5 = 3.6 and (2 + 5 + 4 + 6 + 6)/5 = 4.6. These two values can be combined with other class members' results and a **Histogram**. Then **1-Var Stats** calculated to reveal a distribution centered around a mean of approximately 3.5 and a standard deviation of approximately 1.71/√ (5) = 0.76. You could also work with a sample size of 10 in a similar manner.*

(Tossing five dice, of course, can be simulated with MATH <PRB> 5:randInt(1 , 6 , 5) ENTER.)

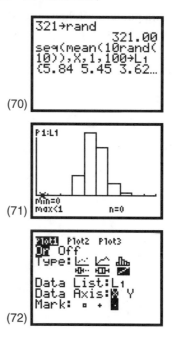

(70)

(71)

(72)

Viewing a Uniform Distribution

Compare the above data to the 100 randomly generated values between 0 and 10, also from Topic 26 (screens 56 and 59), with a **Histogram** that indicates the data could be from a uniformly distributed population (duplicated in screens 74 and 75).

Set up **Plot1** for a normal probability plot (see screen 72), and press ZOOM **9:ZoomStat**. (See screen 76.)

Note that the normal probability plot indicated a symmetric distribution but certainly not a straight line. The points are not more dense in the middle but are uniform throughout. For small x, the n scores (on the y-axis) are more negative than would be expected for a normal distribution. For large x, the n scores are larger than expected.

Viewing a Skewed Distribution

The heights of tall buildings in Philadelphia given in Topic 1 and stored in list **PHILY** have a distribution skewed to the right, as is clear from the **Histogram** repeated here from Topic 1, screen 2. (See screen 77.)

Set up **Plot1** for a normal probability plot with the data list **PHILY**, and then press ZOOM **9:ZoomStat** TRACE for the plot shown in screen 78.

The data points stretched off to the right in screen 78 are a clear indication of the skewness in that direction.

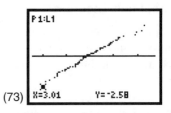

(73)

Note: The x-axis is the data axis. The n score of each data value (x-coordinate) becomes the y-coordinate for the points plotted. (See the reference at the end of this topic.)

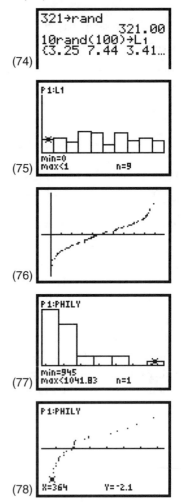

(74)

(75)

(76)

(77)

(78)

Working with Sample Proportions

In Topic 25, the distribution of 100 sample proportions generated from a random binomial distribution with **n** = 30 and $p = 0.67$ was put in a **Histogram** (screens 51 and 52) and is duplicated in screens 79 and 80.

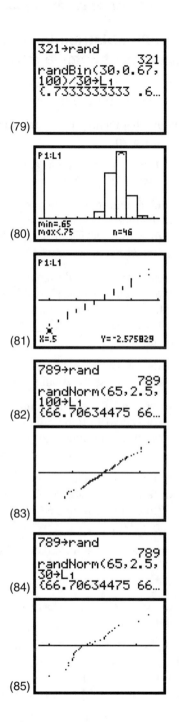

The normal probability plot (screen 81) is fairly straight, but there are groups of points. There are three 0.5s (or 15/30) at the lower left. (Press [TRACE], and use ▶ to see the coordinates.) There are only two 0.533s (or 16/30), but eleven 0.567s (or 17/30) at the other end with one 0.833 (or 25/30) and two 0.867s (or 26/30).

Having stacks of points is called *granularity*. In this case, granularity occurs because we only expect values close to $p = 0.7$ (or 21/30). Between 15/30 and 27/30, there are only 13 possibilities, so with 100 simulations, we are forced to have multiple values. The distribution becomes more normal-like as both $n * p$ and $n * (1 - p)$ become larger, assuring more possible values.

Using Randomly Generated Normal Values

Three different samples of sizes 100, 30, and 10 were generated randomly from a population with a mean of 65 and a standard deviation of 2.5 using [MATH] **<PRB> 6:randNorm**. (See screens 82, 84, and 86.)

The normal probability plots are given in screens 83, 85, and 87. Notice that as the sample size gets smaller, it is less obvious that the samples are from a normal population. To show the ten points more clearly, note that boxes instead of dots are used in screen 87.

The *Introduction to the Practice of Statistics* by David S. Moore and George P. McCabe (W. H. Freeman and Company) gives a number of examples of using normal probability plots to check if sample data meet the normal distribution stipulations required for some statistical tests.

Topic 28—Distribution of the Difference of Two Independent Sample Means (Simulation)

📖 *For this topic, set the mode for two decimal places. (Refer to "Setting Modes" under Do This First.)*

To show that mean = $\mu_1 - \mu_2$ and standard deviation = $\sqrt{(\sigma_1^2/n_1 + \sigma_2^2/n_2)}$:

1. Set the random seed as explained in Topic 21 and shown in the first two lines of screen 88.

   Pick a random sample of size $n_1 = 3$ from a normal distribution with $\mu_1 = 85$ and $\sigma_1 = 7$ using [MATH] **<PRB> 6:randNorm(** 85 [,] 7 [,] 3 [ENTER] for **88.18**, **80.41**, and **87.88** with a mean of **85.49**.

2. Reset the seed, and then pick 100 such samples and store them in **L1** (as shown in screen 89) using [2nd] [LIST] **<OPS> 5:seq(** [2nd] [LIST] **<MATH> 3:mean(** [MATH] **<PRB> 6:randNorm(** 85 [,] 7 [,] 3 [)] [)] [,] X [,] 1 [,] 100 [)] [STO▸] **L1**.

   This gives a list of means with the first value of **85.49**, which repeats the results in screen 88.

3. Generate 100 random samples of size $n_2 = 4$ from a normal distribution with $\mu_2 = 60$ and $\sigma_2 = 8$, and then store in **L2** the same way you did above, with the first mean of **59.85**, as shown in screen 90.

4. Store the difference using **L1** [−] **L2** [STO▸] **L3** with the first difference of **85.49 - 59.85 = 25.64** rounded a bit differently from the **25.63** shown. (See the last line in screen 90.)

The mean and the standard deviation of **L1** are **85.01** and **3.95**, which are close to the theoretical values of $\mu_1 = 85$ and $\sigma1/\sqrt{(n_1)} = 7/\sqrt{(3)} = \sqrt{(7^2/3)} = 4.04$. (See Topic 26.)

For the sample in **L2**, we have **60.41** and **3.97** compared to 60.00 and 4.00. (See screen 92.)

The mean and the standard deviation of the distribution of our 100 differences in **L3** are **24.60** and **5.54** compared to the theoretical values of $\mu_1 - \mu_2 = 85 - 60 = 25.00$ and $\sqrt{(\sigma_1^2/n_1 + \sigma_2^2/n_2)} = \sqrt{(7^2/3 + 8^2/4)} = 5.69 \neq 4.04 + 4.00$. (See screen 93.)

Note that the variances add and not the standard deviations.

The three stat plots are set up for **Histograms** of the data in **L3**, **L2**, and **L1** with the **WINDOW** and the resulting plot as shown in screens 94 and 95 (text labeling was added later).

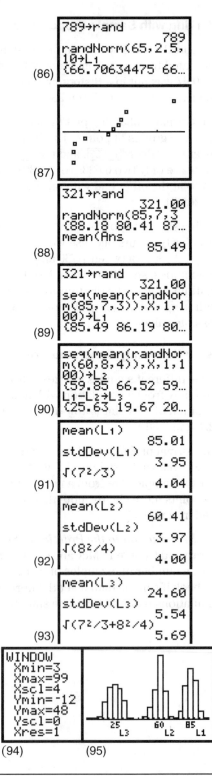

(86)

(87)

(88)

(89)

(90)

(91)

(92)

(93)

(94)   (95)

Topic 29—Geometric Distribution

Assume that 40 percent of a large lot of electrical components are from the ABA Company. If components are selected at random:

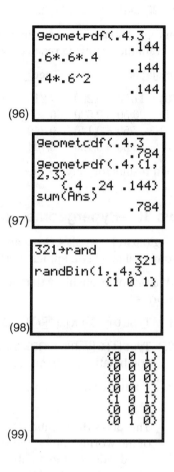

(96)

(97)

(98)

(99)

A. What is the probability that a component from ABA will first be selected on the third pick?

Press 2nd [DIST] **D:geometpdf(** ⊡ **4** ⊡ **3** ENTER for **.144**, as shown in screen 96.

B. What is the probability that an ABA component will be one of the first three components picked?

For P(1) + P(2) + P(3), press 2nd [DIST] **E:geometcdf(** ⊡ **4** ⊡ **3** ENTER for **.784**, as shown on the first two lines in screen 97. (The remainder of the screen gives an alternate method.)

Determining the Probability: Simulation

1. Set the seed as shown in Topic 21 using **321** STO▸ MATH **<PRB> 1:rand** ENTER. (See the first two lines of screen 98.)

2. Use MATH **<PRB> 7:randBin(1** ⊡ ⊡ **4** ⊡ **3** ENTER, as discussed in Topic 21.

    The result is **{1 0 1}**, where the **1** represents selecting an ABA component and a **0** represents a component from another company. (See the last line of screen 98.)

    For each of the three selections, there is a 40 percent chance of selecting an ABA component.

3. Clear the screen, and press ENTER seven times for the results in screen 99.

    •   The first simulation (screen 98) and the sixth simulation (fifth line of screen 99) had a component selected on the *first* pick.

    •   The second and fifth simulations had a component selected for the first time on the *third* pick.

    •   The third, fourth, and seventh simulations had *zero* components selected in three picks.

    •   The eighth simulation had a component selected on the *second* pick.

The approximate probabilities with only eight tries are thus $P(0) = 3/8 = 0.375$, $P(1) = 2/8 = 0.25$, $P(2) = 1/8 = 0.125$, and $P(3) = 2/8 = 0.25$.

If you repeat step 3 six more times and combine the results, you obtain the following results and comparison with theory.

Simulation	Theory
$P(0) = 11/50 = 0.220$	0.216
$P(1) = 26/50 = 0.520$	0.400
$P(2) = 7/50 = 0.140$	0.240
$P(3) = 6/50 = 0.120$	0.144

Not bad results for only 50 tries.

Topic 30—Hypergeometric Distribution

In a bag of twelve apples, three apples have worms. If you randomly selected two apples (without replacement),

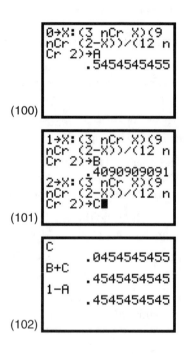

(100)

(101)

(102)

A. What is the probability that neither apple will have worms?

1. Type **0** [STO▸] **X** [ALPHA] [:] (above the ⬚ key).

2. Type [(] **3** [MATH] **<PRB> 3:nCr** (as discussed under combinations in Topic 22).

3. Continue as shown in screen 100, storing the results in **A**.

   This takes the number of ways you can pick none of the wormy apples and two of the good apples and divides by the number of ways you can pick any two apples for $P(0) = 0.545$.

B. What is the probability that at least one apple has a worm in it?

In screen 100, use the [2nd] [ENTRY] feature to change the **0** to a **1** and the **A** to a **B** for $P(1) = .409$. In a similar manner, $P(2) = .045$ so that $P(1) + P(2) = 0.454$. (See screens 101 and 102.)

Determining the Probability: Simulation

1. Set the seed as shown in Topic 21 using **321** [STO▶] [MATH] **<PRB> 1:rand** [ENTER]. (See the first two lines of screen 103.)

2. Use [MATH] **<PRB> 5:randInt (1** [,] **12** [,] **2** [ENTER], as discussed in Topic 19, for two random integers between 1 and 12. Let **1**, **2**, and **3** represent the apples with worms and **4** and **12** those without.

   The result of **{4 9}** is given in the last line of screen 103.

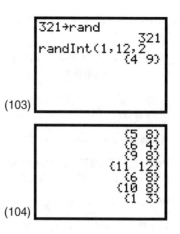

(103)

3. Clear the screen, and press [ENTER] seven times for the results in screen 104.

   It is not until the eighth and last simulation of **{1 3}** that we pick a wormy apple, and then we get two.

(104)

   The approximate probabilities with only eight tries are thus $P(0) = 7/8 = 0.875$, $P(1) = 0/8 = 0$, and $P(2) = 1/8 = 0.125$.

If you repeat step 3 six more times and combine the results, you obtain the following results and comparison with theory.

Simulation	Theory
$P(0) = 30/50 = 0.600$	0.545
$P(1) = 18/50 = 0.360$	0.409
$P(2) = 2/50 = 0.040$	0.045

Not bad results for only 50 tries.

Topic 31—Poisson Distribution

If the mean number of accidents at a given intersection is 2.3 per month,

A. What is the probability of having exactly two accidents for a given month?

Press 2nd [DISTR] **B:poissonpdf(2 ⬚ 3 ⬚ 2** ENTER for P(2) = **.265**. (See screen 105.)

B. What is the probability of having at most two accidents?

Press 2nd [DISTR] **C:poissoncdf(2 ⬚ 3 ⬚ 2** ENTER for P(0) + P(1) + P(2) = **.596**. (See screens 106 and 107.)

C. What is the probability of having at least two accidents?

For P(2) + P(3) + P(4) + P(5) +... = 1 - (P(0) + P(1)) = 1 - **poissoncdf(2.3,1)** = **.669**. (See screen 108.)

D. What is the probability of having from two to four accidents?

For P(2) + P(3) + P(4) = (P(0) + P(1) + P(2) + P(3) + P(4)) - (P(0) + P(1)) = **poissoncdf(2.3,4)** - **poissoncdf(2.3,1)** = **.585**. (See screen 109.)

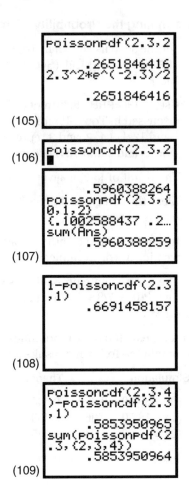

(105)

(106)

(107)

(108)

(109)

Topic 32—Exponential Distribution

Assume that the shelf-life of cake is exponentially distributed with a mean of $\mu = 4$ days. What proportion of the cakes put on the shelf today would you expect to still be fresh 5 days from now?

$P(a \le x \le b) = \mathbf{e}^{\wedge}(-a/\mu) - \mathbf{e}^{\wedge}(-b/\mu)$

$P(5 \le x < \text{E99}) =$ 2nd [e^x] (-) 5 ÷ 4) − 2nd [e^x] (-) E99 ÷ 4) = .2865 (See screen 110.)

The 2nd [e^x] key is in the first column above LN.
E99 represents infinity or a very large number, as given in Do This First in the beginning of this handbook.

Exponential pdf: f(x) = (1/µ) * e^(-x/µ)

$f(0) = 1/\mu = 1/4 = 0.25 = \textbf{Ymax}$ (approximation)

Put the **pdf** in the **Y=** editor as shown in screen 111, set the **WINDOW** as shown in screen 112, and press TRACE for the plot shown in screen 113.

To shade the area of interest, press 2nd [DRAW] **7:Shade(0** ,
Y1 , **5** , **20**) ENTER (screen 114) for the shaded region shown in screen 115. **Y1** is pasted from **VARS <Y-VARS> 1:Function 1:Y1**.

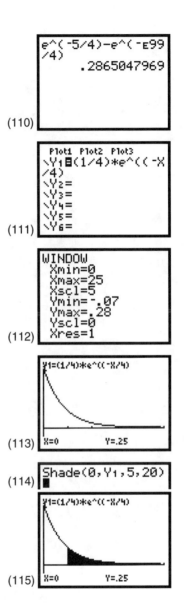

(110)

(111)

(112)

(113)

(114)

(115)

Activity 7

Estimating and Finding Confidence Intervals

This activity begins with estimating the mean of a population with a normal distribution using a simple random sample from that population.

📖 It is important that you read Topic 33 *before* the other topics in Activity 7 because it explains the functions under the **STAT TESTS** menu, the notation, and the meaning of a "confidence interval." You will be using these things in making other estimates.

The last topic in this activity, Topic 39, covers the idea of biased and unbiased estimators with a simulation that explains why we divide by (**n-1**) when calculating the sample standard deviation.

📖 The topic number of the related hypothesis test topic is given in parenthesis after the estimation topic number. For example, the (40) after Topic 33 below indicates that Topic 40 is the related hypothesis test topic for Topic 33.

Topic 33 (40)—Estimating A Normal Population Mean μ (σ Known)

A random sample of size 10 from a population of heights that has a normal distribution (with $\sigma = 2.5$ inches) is given below (with the sample mean).

Store this data in **L₁**.

$$\{66.71, 66.27, 62.81, 66.92, 62.91,$$
$$71.42, 67.39, 63.79, 65.81, 62.81\} = \textbf{L}_1$$

$$\bar{x} = 65.68 \qquad n = 10$$

What is the 80 percent confidence interval for the population mean?

Activity 7, Estimations and Confidence Intervals (cont.)

There are two possible methods of input, depending on how the data is presented to you in a problem. Sometimes all the data is given and it can be stored in a list. Sometimes only the summary stats are given, such as x̄ and **n,** and you must work with these. This activity shows you how to work with both.

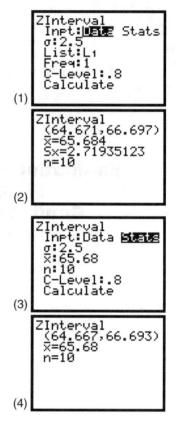

1. Press STAT <TESTS> 7:ZInterval for one of the two possible screens (see screen 1 or 3), depending on what input (**Inpt:**) is highlighted.

2. Enter the correct values from above, highlight **Calculate** in the last row, and then press ENTER for output screen 2 or 4.

We are 80 percent confident that the population mean lies between **64.67** and **66.7** inches.

Home Screen Calculations

What formula was used by the above procedure?

1. With a confidence level of **C** = **0.80**, there is $(1 - 0.80)/2 = 0.10$, or 10 percent of the area in each tail of the probability distribution of sample means.

2. To find the "critical z value" that divides the upper 10 percent from the lower 90 percent, use 2nd [DISTR] 3:**invNorm(0** · **90**) ENTER for **1.28** as shown in screen 5.

3. The "margin of error" **E** is 1.28 times the standard deviation of the sample means, or **E** $= 1.28 * \sigma/\sqrt{(n)} =$ **1.28** ∗ **2.5/√(10) = 1.01** as shown in screen 6.

    Note that the margin of error can be calculated from the confidence interval above by subtracting the mean from the larger value of the interval, or $66.69 - 65.68 = 1.01$.

The confidence interval becomes x̄ ± **E**, or 65.68 ± 1.01, or $65.68 - 1.01$ to $65.68 + 1.01$, or 64.67 to 66.69 as before.

Note: *The slight differences shown in the intervals in screen 2 and 4 are because the sample mean calculated from the Data List had three decimal places*
(x̄ = 65.684) while the stats version was rounded to x̄ = 65.68.

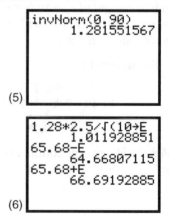

The Meaning of Confidence Interval (Simulation)

The above sample was randomly generated from a normal distribution with a mean of **65** inches and a standard deviation of **2.5** inches (the first interval in screen 7), so the confidence interval of 64.67 to 66.69 did, in fact, contain the population mean. However, we take a sample to estimate the population mean because we do not know it. How confident can we be of our answer?

In the above case, we can be 80 percent confident because if we took all possible samples of size 10 and calculated the confidence intervals as above, 80 percent of these intervals calculated would contain the correct population mean. In screens 7-17 we generate just ten samples, and seven of the ten contain the true mean. (We did not expect exactly eight of ten for so few tries.) The intervals that miss the true mean (screens 11, 13, and 17) miss by 1.01, 0.37 and 0.57 inches.

The sample means are shown as gaps in the middle of the confidence interval lines drawn beneath the normal plot in screen 18 for the ten samples generated. Only when the sample means are in the shaded regions (10 percent in each tail) will the margin of error not be long enough to reach the population mean (the vertical line at **65** inches). Thus, 80 percent of the sample means in this distribution of sample means will be close enough to the population mean for its confidence interval to contain it.

To generate the random samples and calculate the confidence intervals as was done in screens 7-17, proceed as follows.

1. Set the random seed as explained in Topic 21 and shown in the first two lines of screen 7.

2. Complete screen 7 by pressing [MATH] **<PRB>**
    6:randNorm(65 [,] 2 [,] 5 [,] 10 **)** [STO▶] L₁ [ALPHA] [:]
    (above the [.]; ties generating the sample and calculating the confidence together in one statement).

3. Press [2nd] [CATALOG]. Notice the **A** (in the upper right corner of the screen) indicating you are in alpha mode.

4. Press **Z** [▼] [▼] [▼] to point out **ZInterval**, and then press [ENTER]. This pastes it to the home screen. Finish the line by typing 2 [.] 5 [,] L₁ [,] 0 [,] 80.

5. Press [ENTER] to generate the first sample and calculate the confidence interval (**64.671**, **66.697**) as shown in screen 8.

6. Press [ENTER] to take the next sample and calculate the confidence interval (**63.237**, **65.263**) as in screen 9. Continue pressing [ENTER] for the rest of the 10 intervals as in screens 10-17.

(7)
```
789→rand
                   789
randNorm(65,2.5,
10)→L₁:ZInterval
2.5,L₁,0.80█
```

(8)
```
ZInterval
 (64.671,66.697)
x̄=65.6836649
Sx=2.719545079
n=10
```

(9)
```
ZInterval
 (63.237,65.263)
```

(10)
```
ZInterval
 (63.158,65.184)
```

(11)
```
ZInterval
 (61.96,63.986)
```

(12)
```
ZInterval
 (64.602,66.629)
```

(13)
```
ZInterval
 (62.608,64.635)
```

(14)
```
ZInterval
 (63.998,66.024)
```

(15)
```
ZInterval
 (64.049,66.075)
```

(16)
```
ZInterval
 (63.164,65.191)
```

(17)
```
ZInterval
 (65.567,67.593)
x̄=66.57987366
Sx=1.474822824
n=10
```

(18)

Topic 34 (41)—Estimating a Population Mean μ (σ Unknown)

A random sample of size 10 from a population of heights that has a normal distribution is given below (with the sample mean and the standard deviation).

Store this data in **L1**.

{66.71, 66.27, 62.81, 66.92, 62.91, 71.42, 67.39, 63.79, 65.81, 62.81} = **L1**

x̄ = 65.68, **Sx** = 2.72, **n** = 10

What is the 90 percent confidence interval for the population mean?

1. Press ⌈STAT⌋ **<TESTS> 8:TInterval** for one of the two possible screens (see screen 19 or 21), depending on what input (**Inpt:**) is highlighted.

2. Enter the correct values as above, highlight **Calculate** in the last row, and then press ⌈ENTER⌋ for output screen 20 or 22.

We are 90 percent confident that the population mean lies between **64.1** and **67.26** inches.

Home Screen Calculations

To find the "critical *t* value" with the TI-83, there is no **invT** like the **invNorm**, so we will use the equation solver at the end of this topic to show a value of **1.833** (or you can look it up in a table).

The margin of error is calculated very much like in Topic 33, but now **Sx** is used instead of σ for a value of 1.58. Or, from the previous interval, subtract the mean from the upper interval value (67.26 - 65.68 = 1.58). From screen 23, we also see that the confidence interval is **64.10** to **67.26** as above, with the width of the interval 67.26 - 64.10 = 3.16, or twice the margin of error (2 ∗ 1.58).

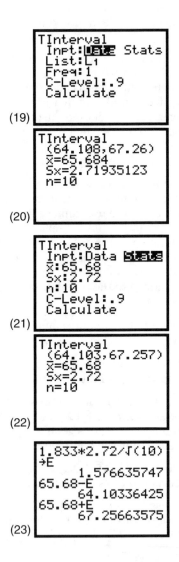

(19)

(20)

(21)

(22)

(23)

Notice the interval above is wider than the one shown in screen 24 for an 80 percent confidence interval (66.87 - 64.50 = 2.37). (The **Inpt** screen is not shown, but is like screen 19 with **C-Level: .8**.) The wider the interval for a given sample size, the more confident we are of the interval reaching the population mean.

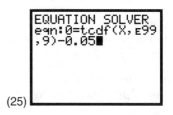

(24)

Topic 33 used the same data but used a known σ and obtained an 80 percent confidence interval of 64.67 to 66.69 for a width of 2.02 inches (66.69 - 64.67 = 2.02 inches). The interval above is wider for two reasons: the critical t is bigger than the critical z (1.833 compared to 1.28) and **Sx** is bigger than σ (2.72 compared to 2.50). The **Sx** will change from sample to sample, so it is possible that the interval width could sometimes be smaller than the σ case. If we consider all the possible variable width intervals, 80 percent will contain the true population mean.

Using the Equation Solver for Critical t Values

For a 90 percent confidence interval, there is an area of $(1 - 0.90)/2 = 0.05$ in each tail. We want to solve **tcdf(X, E99, 9)** = **0.05** for X, the X that gives the area of 0.05 in the right tail (from **X** to **E99**) of a t distribution with nine degrees of freedom ($n - 1 = 10 - 1 = 9$).

1. Press MATH **0:Solver** for screen 25. If your screen does not start with **EQUATION SOLVER**, you must first press ▲.

2. Enter your equation using 2nd [DISTR] **5:tcdf(X ⎵ E99 ⎵ 9) − 0 . 05**.

3. Press ENTER, and modify the screen to look like screen 26.

   We pick **X = 2** for t as a reasonable first guess in the right tail. The bound will probably show as **{-1E99, 1E99}**, which works fine; although you could restrict it to positive values by making it **{0, 1E99}**.

4. With the cursor blinking on or after the **2**, press ALPHA [SOLVE].

   Notice the busy signal while the equation is being solved numerically. Then screen 27 appears showing a critical t value of **1.833**.

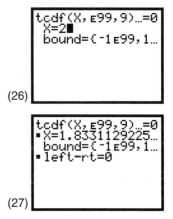

(25)

Note: We write the equation to be solved as $0 = tcdf(X, E99, 9) - 0.05$ to meet the requirements of the Solver.

(26)

(27)

       STATISTICS HANDBOOK FOR THE **TI-83**

Topic 35 (42)—Estimating a Population Proportion

A random poll of 265 people from a population of interest found 73.2 percent agreement with a public policy. What is the 95 percent confidence interval for the proportion in the whole population who would agree? (Note that $265*.732 \geq 10$ and $265(1-.732) \geq 10$, so a normal distribution can be used to approximate a binomial.)

1. Press [STAT] **<TESTS> A:1-PropZInt** for screen 28.

    The input screen is looking for the number who agreed (x), and this was not given in this particular problem.

2. Let the TI-83 do the calculation for you ($265*.732$). However, when you leave this line, the calculation reveals a noninteger, **193.98** (see screen 29).

3. Highlight **Calculate** in the last row, and press [ENTER].

    A **DOMAIN** error results.

4. As shown in screen 30, round the value to the nearest integer (**194**), highlight **Calculate** in the last row, and press [ENTER] for screen 31.

We are 95 percent confident that between 67.88 to 78.54 percent of the population agree with the public policy.

Home Screen Calculations

The margin of error is $.7854 - .7321 = .0533$ as shown in screen 32. The confidence interval is calculated in screen 33.

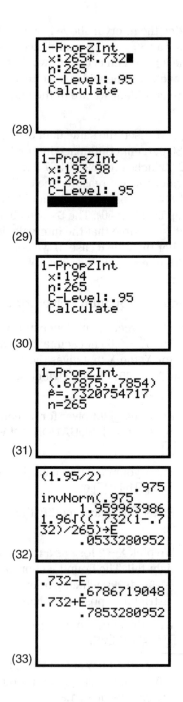

(28)

(29)

(30)

(31)

(32)

(33)

Finding a Sample Size

What size sample would be needed to reduce the margin of error in the above problem from 0.0533 to 0.02, or 2 percent?

Solving for n in our margin of error equation, we have $n = \mathbf{1.96^2}$ $\mathbf{* 0.732(1 - 0.732)/0.02^2 = 1885}$ (rounding up). (See screen 34.)

The original sample was generated (as described in Topic 25 and shown in screen 35) from a population with a population proportion of 0.70. Thus the interval obtained (67.88 to 78.54 percent) does contain the 70 percent. (See screen 35.)

For the larger sample (**n = 1885**) shown in screen 36, the resulting 0.713 is within 0.02 of 0.70.

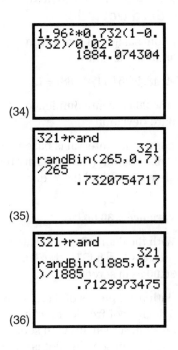

(34)

(35)

(36)

Topic 36 (43)—Estimating a Normal Population Standard Deviation σ

A random sample of size 4 from a population that is normally distributed is as follows.

{54.54, 43.44, 54.11, 46.88} = **L1**.

Find the 90 percent confidence interval for the population standard deviation.

The confidence interval is based on the sample variance and the χ^2 distribution (the similarity between the distribution of sample variance and the χ^2 distribution can be seen in Topic 39).

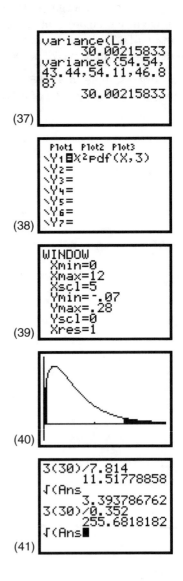

(37)

A. Variance = **30.00**.

With the data in **L1**, calculate the variance of the data by pressing [2nd] [LIST] <MATH>8:variance(L1 [ENTER] for **30.00** as in screen 37.

(38)

With $n = 4$ pieces of data, we will be using $n - 1 = 4 - 1 = 3$ degrees of freedom for the χ^2 distribution. The plot is given in screen 40 (with setup as in screens 38 and 39). As you can see, the plot is skewed to the right. Because it is not symmetrical, two critical values are needed, $\chi^2 L$ and $\chi^2 R$, for left and right. (Shading was done with [2nd] [DRAW] **7:Shade(0** ⬚ **Y1** ⬚ **0** ⬚ **0** ⬚ **35** ⬚ and **Shade(0** ⬚ **Y1** ⬚ **7** ⬚ **8** ⬚ **E99.**) Thus, 5 percent of each tail is shaded. See statement 2.)

(39)

B. Critical values are $\chi^2 L$ = **0.352** and $\chi^2 R$ = **7.814**.

You can look up the critical values in a table (with 0.05 in each tail of the distribution), or you can obtain them using the equation solver as explained at the end of this topic.

(40)

C. Confidence intervals for variance = 11.52, 255.68.

Lower value = $(n - 1)Sx^2/\chi^2 R$ = 3 ∗ 30.00/7.814 = **11.52**
Upper value = $(n - 1)Sx^2/\chi^2 L$ = 3 ∗ 30.00/0.352 = **255.68**

D. Confidence interval for standard deviation = 3.39, 15.99.

Lower value = $\sqrt{((n - 1)Sx^2/\chi^2 R)}$ = $\sqrt{(11.52)}$ = **3.39**
Upper value = $\sqrt{((n - 1)Sx^2/\chi^2 L)}$ = $\sqrt{(255.68)}$ = **15.99**

(41)

The above sample was the first of 100 randomly generated samples in Topic 39 from a normal distribution with a variance $\sigma^2 = 100$ and a standard deviation $\sigma = 10$. These, in fact, do lie in the intervals calculated. The intervals are quite wide, but they are based on a very small sample.

Using the Equation Solver for Critical Values χ^2L and χ^2R

We want to solve the following equations for X such that the area (from 0 to X and from X to the very large number E99) is **0.05** under a χ^2 distribution with $n - 1 = 4 - 1 = 3$ degrees of freedom.

(i) χ^2**cdf(0, X, 3) = 0.05**
(ii) χ^2**cdf(X, E99, 3) = 0.05**

For χ^2L:

1. Press [MATH] **0:Solver** for screen 42. If your screen does not start with **EQUATION SOLVER**, you must first press [▲].

2. To meet the requirements of the solver, write equation (i) as in screen 42 using [2nd] [DISTR] **7: χ^2cdf(**.

3. Press [ENTER] and modify the screens to look like screen 43.

   We pick **X = 1** for our first guess for the left tail. The bounds will probably show as **{-1E99, 1E99}**, which works fine, although we could restrict them to positive values **{0, 1E99}** because χ^2 cannot be negative.

4. With the cursor blinking on or after **X = 1**, press [ALPHA] [SOLVE].

   The critical value **X = 0.352** = χ^2L is calculated. See screen 44. (During calculations, a busy signal shows in the upper-right corner of the screen.)

For χ^2R:

Repeat the above procedure for the second equation (ii) as in screen 45. Use a first guess of **10**, as in screen 46, for the critical value χ^2R = **7.815** as in screen 47.

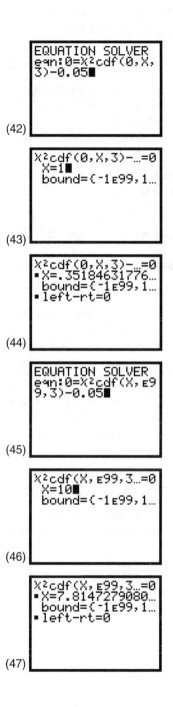

(42)

(43)

(44)

(45)

(46)

(47)

Topic 37 (44)—Estimating the Difference in Two Population Means

Estimating Independent Samples

A study designed to estimate the difference in the mean test scores that result from using two different teaching methods obtained the following data from two random samples of students taught with the two methods.

							mean	Sx	n
Method A (L$_1$)	40	38	39	32	35	38	37	2.966	6
Method B (L$_2$)	34	36	31	37	29		33.4	3.362	5

Store the above data in **L$_1$** and **L$_2$**, and calculate the 95 percent confidence interval for the difference in the population means.

TInterval (σ1 and σ2 Unknown)

Assume the above data is from normal populations.

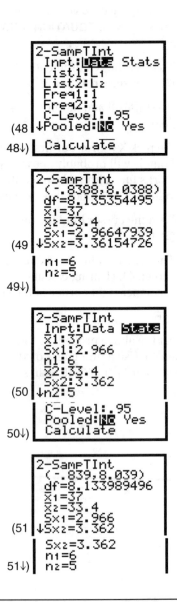

1. Press STAT <**TESTS**> **0:2-SampTInt** for screens 48 and 50 (48↓ and 50↓ are the second page of the input screens obtained by using ▾).

    Screens 48 and 50 do not pool the sample variances as does screen 52. (For the pooled case, see "To Pool or Not to Pool" on the next page.) Screen 48 uses the **Data List**. However, for screen 50, you must enter the summary **Stats** of means, standard deviation, and sample sizes.

2. Make the entries as shown in screen 48 or 50, highlight **Calculate**, and press ENTER for screens 49 or 51.

The 95 percent confidence interval for the difference of the means is **-0.839** to **8.039** for the non-pooled case. Because zero is in the interval, there could be no difference in the mean test scores for the two groups, or Method A could have a higher mean than Method B (a positive difference), or Method B could have a higher mean than Method A (a negative difference). Perhaps larger samples would clarify the situation.

To Pool or Not to Pool

Screens 52 and 53 give the input and output for the pooled procedure with a 95 percent confidence interval of -.7124 to **7.9124**.

The pooled procedure is appropriate if σ1 = σ2. It is not appropriate to pool if σ1 ≠ σ2.

Some statistics textbooks only give the pooled version because before the TI-83, the noninteger value for degrees of freedom that results from the non-pooled procedure was difficult to handle without a computer.

If you are not sure that σ1 = σ2, then it is safe to use the non-pooled procedure because it will always give a conservative answer. (The confidence interval will be a little wider than in the pooled case (-.839 to 8.039 compared to -.7124 to 7.9124.))

ZInterval (σ1 and σ2 Known)

Assume the above data is from normal populations but that σ1 = **2.966** and σ2 = **3.362**.

1. Press [STAT] <TESTS> 9:2-SampZint for screen 54.

    The **Data Lists** input is also possible, but only the **Stats** version is shown. Some texts use this procedure for large samples when σ1 and σ2 can be approximated by **Sx1** and **Sx2**.

2. Make the entries as shown in screen 54, highlight **Calculate,** and then press [ENTER] for the output shown in screen 55.

The 95 percent confidence interval for the difference of the means is **-0.184** to **7.384**. This interval is similar to, but not as wide as, the **Tintervals** above.

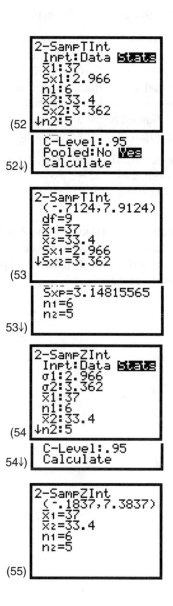

(52

52↓)

(53

53↓)

(54

54↓)

(55)

Home Screen Calculations

Screens 56, 57, and 58 show the non-pooled **TInterval**. First, the degrees of freedom (**8.134**) are calculated; second, with $(1 - .95)/2 = 0.025$ in each tail, the critical t value of **2.299** is checked. (The critical t value is calculated by using the equation solver to solve **tcdf(X, E99, 8.134) = 0.025** for **X = 8.134**, as explained in "Home Screen Calculations" in Topic 34.) Next, the margin of error and confidence interval are calculated.

Screens 59, 60, and 61 are for the pooled case with degrees of freedom = $n1 + n2 - 2 = 6 + 5 - 2 = 9$ and a critical value of **2.262** (from a table or using the procedure explained in Topic 34).

Screens 62 and 63 are for the **ZInterval**. Note that the calculation for the **ZInterval** confidence interval is the same as for the non-pooled **TInterval** except for the differences in the critical z and t values.

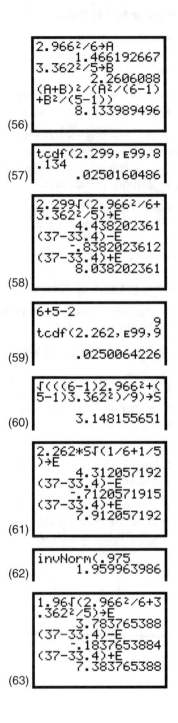

(56)
```
2.966²/6→A
         1.466192667
3.362²/5→B
         2.2606088
(A+B)²/(A²/(6-1)
+B²/(5-1))
         8.133989496
```

(57)
```
tcdf(2.299,E99,8
.134
         .0250160486
```

(58)
```
2.299√(2.966²/6+
3.362²/5)→E
         4.438202361
(37-33.4)-E
         -.8382023612
(37-33.4)+E
         8.038202361
```

(59)
```
6+5-2
               9
tcdf(2.262,E99,9
         .0250064226
```

(60)
```
√(((6-1)2.966²+(
5-1)3.362²)/9)→S
         3.148155651
```

(61)
```
2.262*S√(1/6+1/5
)→E
         4.312057192
(37-33.4)-E
         -.7120571915
(37-33.4)+E
         7.912057192
```

(62)
```
invNorm(.975
         1.959963986
```

(63)
```
1.96√(2.966²/6+3
.362²/5)→E
         3.783765388
(37-33.4)-E
         -.1837653884
(37-33.4)+E
         7.383765388
```

Estimating Dependent Samples

To test a blood pressure medication, the diastolic blood pressure readings of a random sample of ten people with high blood pressure were recorded. After a few weeks on the medication, their pressures were recorded again.

See the data recorded in the table below. The mean and the standard deviation of the differences in **L3** were calculated with **1-Var Stats** as explained in Topic 4 and shown in screens 64 and 65. Note that the mean of the differences is **5.9** and the standard deviation of the differences is **5.666**.

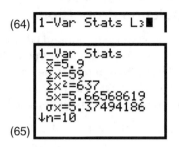

(64)

(65)

Subject		1	2	3	4	5	6	7	8	9	10
Before	**(L₁)**:	94	87	105	92	102	85	110	95	92	93
After	**(L₂)**:	87	88	93	87	92	88	96	87	92	86
L₁ - L₂ = L₃		7	-1	12	5	10	-3	14	8	0	7

Assume the diastolic blood pressure readings are normally distributed, and calculate the 95 percent confidence interval for the mean difference in pressure.

1. Press STAT **<TESTS> 8:TInterval** for one of the two possible screens (see screen 66 or 68), depending on what input (**Inpt:**) is highlighted.

2. Put in the correct values as above, highlight **Calculate** in the last row, and then press ENTER for the output in screens 67 or 69.

We are 95 percent confident that the difference in the population mean lies between 1.85 and 9.95 units of pressure, and this indicates that the medication seems to have some effect.

Home screen calculations are similar to those done in Topic 34.

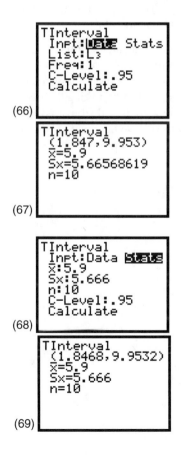

(66)

(67)

(68)

(69)

Topic 38 (45)—Estimating the Difference in Two Population Proportions

A polling organization found 694 of 936 (694/936 = 74.15 percent) women sampled agreed with a public policy while 645 of 941 (68.54 percent) men agreed. Find the 95 percent confidence interval for the difference in the proportions between the two populations sampled.

Women: x1 = 694   n1 = 936

Men: x2 = 645   n2 = 941

1. Press ⌷STAT⌷ <TESTS> **B:2-PropZInt** for screen 70.

2. Enter the correct values (as in screen 70), highlight **Calculate** in the last row, and then press ⌷ENTER⌷ for the output in screen 71.

We are 95 percent confident that the difference in population proportions lies between 1.52 and 9.68 percent. This indicates that a larger proportion of women are in agreement with the policy than are men.

Home screen calculations are given in screens 72 and 73 with the critical z value of **1.96** and a margin of error of **4.08** percent. These calculations also could have been obtained from screen 71 by taking 0.0968 - (0.7415 - 0.6854) = .0407. The confidence interval from 1.53 to 9.69 percent differs slightly from the above because of rounding.

Note: n1 = 936 = 694 + 242 (both values greater than 5). n2 = 941 = 645 + 296 (both values greater than 5). Therefore, the normal approximation to the binomial can be used.

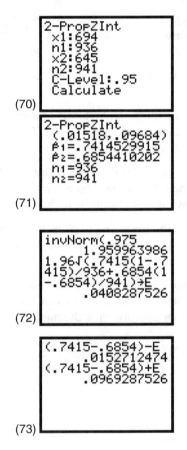

(70)

(71)

(72)

(73)

Topic 39—Unbiased and Biased Estimators (Simulation)

📖 *For this topic, set the mode for two decimal places. (Refer to "Setting Modes" under Do This First.)*

A sample statistic used to estimate a population parameter is *unbiased* if the mean of the sampling distribution of the statistic is equal to the true value of the parameter being estimated.

You saw in Topic 24 that the sample proportion is an unbiased estimator of the population proportion. In Topic 25, you saw that the sample mean is an unbiased estimator of the population mean. In this topic, you will see that $\Sigma(x - \bar{x})^2/n$ is a *biased* estimator of the population variance while $\Sigma(x - \bar{x})^2/(n-1)$ is unbiased.

Because **Sx²**, the "variance" on the TI-83, is unbiased (divides by $n - 1$), you will need to change to biased (maximum likelihood estimator) by multiplying by $(n - 1)/n$ as $((n - 1)/n) * \Sigma(x - \bar{x})^2/(n - 1) = \Sigma(x - \bar{x})^2/n$. For **n = 4**, you would multiply by 3/4 or 0.75.

After making the above change, proceed as follows.

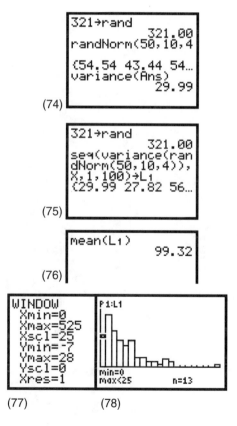

(74)

(75)

(76)

(77)   (78)

1. Set the random seed as explained in Topic 21 and shown in the first two lines in screen 74.

2. Press MATH <PRB>6:randNorm(50 □, 10 □, 4 ENTER to simulate picking four values from a normal distribution with a mean of 50 and a standard deviation of 10 or a variance of $10^2 = 100$. The values are **54.54**, **43.44**, **54.11**, and **46.88** (middle values in screen 74).

3. Press 2nd [LIST] <MATH> 8:variance(2nd [ANS] ENTER for **29.99**, an unbiased variance of these values (last value in screen 74).

4. Reset the seed and generate a sequence of 100 sample variances. Store these in **L₁**, as in screen 75, with **seq** pasted from 2nd [LIST] <OPS> 5. Notice that the first variance is **29.99** as above.

5. Obtain the mean of **L₁** by pressing 2nd [LIST] <MATH> 3:mean(L₁ ENTER, as in screen 76. The **99.32** is very close to the population value of 100.

6. Set up **Plot1** for a **Histogram** of the data in **L₁** (as explained in Topic 1) with the **WINDOW** shown in screen 77 for the results in screen 78.

For the biased estimator, you can multiply each of the unbiased calculations for the variance by **0.75** as explained earlier and as shown in screen 79. These have a mean of **74.49**, which is not near the population value of 100.

The remaining screens (80, 81, and 82) give the procedure and results if you had started from scratch in calculating the biased estimator with the mean and a **Histogram** of your sample distribution. Note that the sample distribution is skewed to the right. This is not surprising when you realize that the left is bounded by zero because the variance is a sum of squares and, thus, can never be negative. The χ^2 distribution is related to this distribution and is discussed in Topic 36.

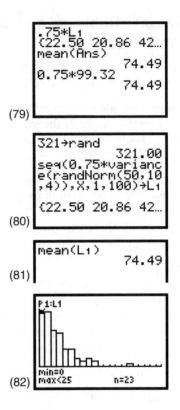

(79)

(80)

(81)

(82)

Activity 8

Testing Hypotheses (Means, Proportions, and Standard Deviations)

This activity starts with testing a hypothesis about a population mean with σ known (Topic 40).

📖 It is important that you read Topic 40 because it explains the STAT <TESTS> functions for testing hypotheses as well as the general format that will be used with the other topics in this part.

📖 The topic number of the related estimation topic is given in parenthesis after the hypothesis topic number. For example, (33) after Topic 40 below indicates that Topic 33 is the related estimation topic for Topic 40.

Topic 40 (33)—Testing Hypothesis of a Population Mean μ (σ Known)

A random sample of size 10 from a population of heights that has a normal distribution (with σ = 2.5 inches) is given below (with the sample mean). The sample was taken to test the claim that the population has a mean height of 67.25 inches.

Store this data in **L₁**.

$$\{66.71, 66.27, 62.81, 66.92, 62.91,$$
$$71.42, 67.39, 63.79, 65.81, 62.81\} = \mathbf{L_1}$$

$$\bar{x} = 65.68 \qquad n = 10$$

Test: $H_0: \mu = \mu_0 = 67.25$ $H_a: \mu \neq \mu_0 = 67.25$

There are two possible methods of input, depending on how the data is presented to you in a problem. Sometimes, all the data is given, and it can be stored in a list. Sometimes, only the summary stats are given, such as $\bar{x}$ and **n,** and you must work with these. This activity shows you how to work with both.

1. Press STAT <TESTS> 1:Z-Test for one of the two possible screens (see screen 1 or 3), depending on what input (**Inpt:**) is highlighted.

2. Enter the correct values as in screen 1 or 3, highlight **Calculate** or **Draw** in the last row, and then press ENTER.

   If you selected **Calculate,** output screen 2 or 4 is displayed; for **Draw**, a screen like screen 5 is displayed.

With a p-value of about **0.047***, there is good evidence that the null hypothesis should be rejected. Because **z** is negative (**-1.98**), we conclude that the mean of the population is significantly less than 67.25 inches.

The **z** above was calculated as follows.

$z = (\bar{x} - \mu_0)/(\sigma/\sqrt{n}) = (65.68 - 67.25)/(2.5/\sqrt{10}) = $ **-1.9859**

The Meaning of p-value and One- and Two-Tail Test

The above was a two-tail test ($\mu \neq 67.25$). Our sample mean could have been either in the right or the left tail of the distribution of sample means, as shown in screen 5.

If Ha: $\mu < \mu_0 = 67.25$ for the **Stats** input of the **Z-Test**, then the **Draw** output is given in screen 6. Notice that we only consider the left tail. We would never be able to reject the null hypothesis and accept the alternative hypothesis if our sample mean was greater than the hypothesized mean. The p-value for the one-tail case is half of that for the two-tail case.

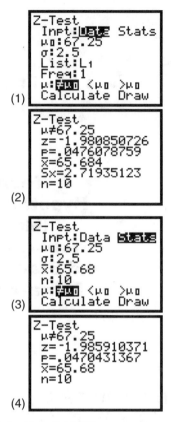

(1)
(2)
(3)
(4)

Note: *The slight differences shown in screens 2 and 4 are because the sample mean calculated from the data list had three decimal places ($\bar{x}$ = 65.684) while the stats version was rounded to $\bar{x}$ = 65.68.*

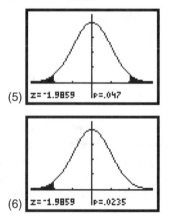

(5) z=-1.9859   p=.047

(6) z=-1.9859   p=.0235

When Ho: $\mu = \mu_0 = 65$ Ha: $\mu > \mu_0 = 65$ and the input of the **Z-Test** is set up as in the screen 7, with the **Draw** output given in screen 8, notice that the sample mean (65.68) is much closer to $\mu_0 = 65$ (65.68 - 65 = +0.68 than in the previous case (65.68 - 67.25 = -1.57). Thus, we would not reject $\mu_0 = 65$ because it is not unusual to have a sample mean of 65.68 when $\mu_0 = 65$. In fact, this could happen about 19.5 percent of the time. (See the p-value in screen 8.)

The plot resulting from screens 9-12 combines the plots in screens 6 and 8 to make the contrast even clearer. (See screen 12.) We are much more likely to reject the notion that our sample mean (65.68) belongs to the distribution with mean 67.25 than one with a mean of 65.

Note that the sample for this topic (stored in **L1**) was randomly generated from a normal distribution with a mean of 65 in Topic 33.

(7)

(8)

(9)

(10)

(11)

(12)

Topic 41 (34)— Testing Hypothesis of a Population Mean μ (σ Unknown)

A random sample of size 10 from a population of heights that has a normal distribution is given below (with the sample mean and the standard deviation).

Store this data in **L₁**.

$$\{66.71, 66.27, 62.81, 66.92, 62.91,$$
$$71.42, 67.39, 63.79, 65.81, 62.81\} = \textbf{L}_1$$

$$\bar{x} = 65.68, \textbf{Sx} = 2.72, \textbf{n} = 10$$

Test: H₀: $\mu = \mu_0 = 67.25$ Hₐ: $\mu \neq \mu_0 = 67.25$

1. Press STAT <**TESTS**> 2:**T-Test** for one of the two possible screens (see screens 13 and 15), depending on what input (**Inpt:**) is highlighted.

2. Enter the correct values as in screen 13 or 15, highlight **Calculate** or **Draw** in the last row, and then press ENTER.

    If you selected **Calculate**, output screen 14 or 16 is displayed; for **Draw**, a screen like screen 17 is displayed.

With a p-value of approximately 0.10 and a negative t statistic, there is some evidence that the population mean is less than 67.25. However, at a significance level of $\alpha = 0.05$, we would not reject the null hypothesis. There is insufficient evidence to reject the null hypothesis even if, in fact, it is not equal to 67.25.

The t above was calculated as follows.

$\textbf{t} = (\bar{x} - \mu_0)/(Sx/\sqrt{n}) = (65.68\text{-}67.25)/(2.72/\sqrt{10}) = \text{-}1.825.$

Since our sample was randomly generated from a normal population with a mean of 65 and a standard deviation of 2.5 (see Topic 33), we should be able to increase our evidence to reject the null hypothesis that the mean is 67.25 by generating a larger sample (of size 20), as shown in screens 18, 19, and 20, with a p-value of 0.0017.

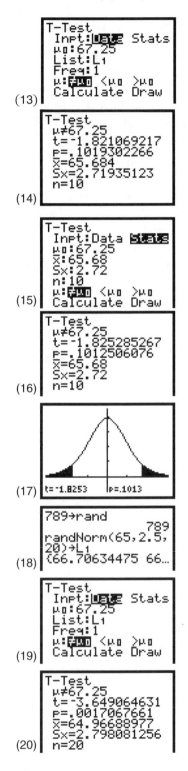

(13)

(14)

(15)

(16)

(17)

(18)

(19)

(20)

Topic 42 (35)—Testing Hypothesis of a Population Proportion

When a public policy was introduced several years ago, 67 percent of the people voted for it. Test the claim that a larger percentage of voters would be in favor of the policy today. A random sample of 265 voters has 73.2 percent agreeing with the policy.

Test: H_0: $p = p_0 = 0.67$ Ha: $p > p_0 = 0.67$

Because $n * p = 265 * 0.732 = 194 > 10$ and $n * (1 - p) = 265 - 194 = 71 > 10$, we can use a normal distribution to approximate the binomial.

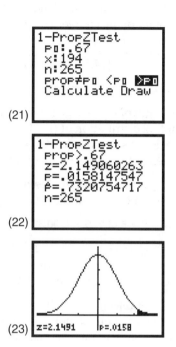

(21)

(22)

(23)

1. Press STAT <TESTS> 5: 1-PropZTest for screen 21.

2. Enter the correct values as in screen 21, highlight **Calculate** or **Draw** in the last row, and then press ENTER.

   If you selected **Calculate,** output screen 22 is displayed; for **Draw,** screen 23 is displayed.

A p-value as small as **0.0158** is strong evidence that the new proportion is probably larger than 67 percent, so we reject the null hypothesis.

The **z** above was calculated as follows.

$z = (0.732 - 0.67)/\sqrt{(0.67 * (1 - .67)/265)} = 2.15$.

Note that in Topic 35 (screen 35), this sample was randomly generated from a population with **p = 0.70** using **randBin(265, 0.7)/265 = 0.732**.

Topic 43 (36)—Testing Hypothesis of a Normal Population Standard Deviation σ

A battery recharger gives a charge with a mean of 50 hours and a standard deviation of 10 hours. An adjustment reduced the variability of the charge. To test it, the following random sample was taken.

$$\{54.54, 43.44, 54.11, 46.88\} = \mathsf{L_1}$$

Test: H₀: σ = 10 Ha: σ < 10

The length of the charge is normally distributed, so the sampling distribution of $(\mathbf{n} - 1)s^2/\sigma^2$ is chi-square distributed. Note that if s^2 is close to σ^2, these values will be close to the degrees of freedom $\mathbf{n} - 1$ (4 - 1 = 3 in this case).

Using [2nd] [LIST] **<MATH> 7:stdDev(L₁** [ENTER], or [STAT] **<CALC>1: 1-Var Stats L₁** [ENTER] gives **Sx = 5.48**.

$\chi^2 = (4 - 1) * 5.48^2/10^2 = 0.90$

Press [2nd] [DISTR] **7: χ² cdf(0** ⬚ **0** ⬚ **90** ⬚ **3** ⬚ [ENTER] to get the left-tail probability of the χ^2 distribution with three degrees of freedom, or the p-value of **0.17457**, as shown in screen 24.

(24)

We do not reject the null hypothesis. There is insufficient evidence from our sample of size 4 to conclude that the variability has, in fact, decreased.

Another method of finding the **p** value is with [2nd] [DISTR] **<DRAW> 3:Shadeχ²**, as shown in screen 26, with results in screen 27 (with the **WINDOW** setup as in screen 25).

(25)

(26)

The above sample was, in fact, randomly generated from a normal distribution with mean 50 and standard deviation 10 (see Topic 39). Therefore, even with larger samples, it is highly possible that we would not be able to reject the null hypothesis.

(27)

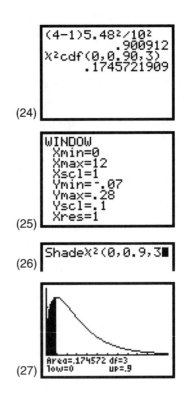

Topic 44 (37)—Testing Hypothesis of Two Population Means

Testing Independent Samples

Test the claim that teaching Method A results in higher test scores than Method B based on the following scores from random samples of students taught with the two methods.

							mean	Sx	n
Method A (L_1)	40	38	39	32	35	38	37	2.966	6
Method B (L_2)	34	36	31	37	29		33.4	3.362	5

Store Method A data in L_1 and Method B data in L_2, and test:

$H_0: \mu_1 = \mu_2$, or $(\mu_1 - \mu_2 = 0)$ $H_a: \mu_1 > \mu_2$ or $(\mu_1 - \mu_2 > 0)$

Two Sample T-Test ($\sigma 1$ and $\sigma 2$ Unknown)

Assume the populations of test scores are normally distributed.

1. Press [STAT] <TESTS> 4:2-SampTTest for screens 28, 30, or 32.

   Screens 28 and 30 do not pool the sample variances, but screen 32 does. (See "To Pool or Not To Pool" in Activity 7, Topic 37.) Screen 28 uses the **Data List**. However, for screens 30 and 32, you must enter the summary **Stats** of means, standard deviations, and sample sizes.

2. Enter the correct values as shown in the screens, highlight **Calculate** or **Draw** and press [ENTER].

   In the examples shown, screen 29 is the **Calculate** output for **Data List** input of screen 28. Screen 31 is the **Draw** output from the **Stats** input of screen 30. (The **Calculate** output from screen 30 would be very close to the output in screen 29). Screen 33 is the **Calculate** output of the pooled **Stats** input of screen 32.)

With a p-value of less than 0.05, there is sufficient evidence to reject the null hypothesis and conclude that Method A has significantly higher mean scores than Method B.

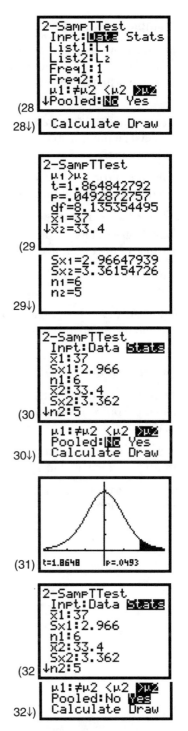

Note: *The **Calculate** output (screen 33) is at the top of the next page.*

Two-Sample Z-Test (σ1 and σ2 Known)

Assume the above data is from normal populations but that σ1 = 2.966 and σ2 = 3.362. (Some texts use this procedure for large samples when σ1 and σ2 can be approximated by **Sx1** and **Sx2**.)

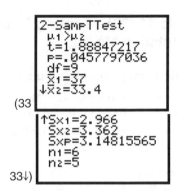

(33

(33↓)

1. Press STAT <TESTS> **3:2-SampZTest** for screen 34. The **Data Lists** input is also possible, but we show only the **Stats** version.

2. Make the entries as shown in screen 34, highlight **Draw**, and then press ENTER for screen 35.

    The z statistic (**1.8648**) in screen 35 is the same as the t statistic in screen 29, but the **p** value is different because of the difference in a z and a t distribution .

We draw the same conclusion as above because a **p** value of **0.0311** is stronger evidence to reject the null hypothesis.

When the variance is not pooled, the calculation of the z statistic and the t statistic is the same with **Sx1** = σ1 and **Sx2** = σ2.

(37 - 33.4)/√(2.966²/6 + 3.362²/5) = 1.8648.

The degrees of freedom for the t case are the same as that calculated in Topic 37, where the same data was used (**df = 8.135**).

When the variance is pooled, **Sxp = 3.148** (the pooled standard deviation) was calculated in Topic 37 and stored as **S**.

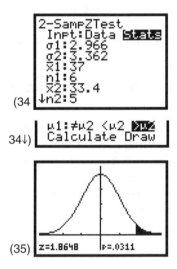

(34

(34↓)

(35)

t = (37 - 33.4)/(3.148 * √(1/6 + 1/5)) = 1.89.
Degrees of freedom = **n1 + n2 - 2 = 6 + 5 - 2 = 9**

Testing Dependent Samples

To test the claim that a blood pressure medication reduces the diastolic blood pressure, a random sample of 10 people with high blood pressure had their pressures recorded. After a few weeks on the medication, their pressures were recorded again. See the data in the table below. The mean and the standard deviation of the differences (stored in **L3**) were calculated with **1-Var Stats** as shown in screens 36 and 37.

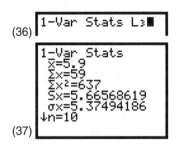

(36)

(37)

Subject	1	2	3	4	5	6	7	8	9	10
Before (L1):	94	87	105	92	102	85	110	95	92	93
After (L2):	87	88	93	87	92	88	96	87	92	86
L1 - L2 = L3	7	-1	12	5	10	-3	14	8	0	7

Assuming the diastolic blood pressure readings are normally distributed, use the following procedure to test the claim with $H_0: \mu_d = 0$ $H_a: \mu_d > 0$.

Note that the mean of the differences is **5.9**, and the standard deviation of the differences is **5.6657** as in screen 37.

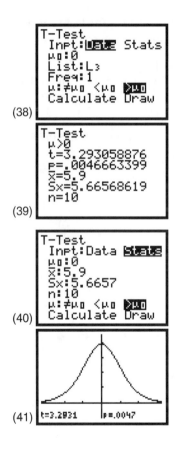

1. Press STAT <TESTS> **2:TTest** and proceed with the differences in **L3**, just as you did for one sample in Topic 41, to get one of the two possible screens (see screen 38 or 40), depending on what input (**Inpt:**) is highlighted.

(38)

(39)

2. Enter the correct values as shown in screen 38 or 40, highlight **Calculate** or **Draw**, and then press ENTER.

    Screen 39 is the **Calculate** output of screen 38. Screen 41 is the **Draw** output of screen 40.

(40)

With such a small **p** value of 0.0047 (off the scale to the right in the plot in screen 41), we reject the null hypothesis. Because the mean difference (and *t* statistic) is positive and the differences were obtained by subtracting the *after* from the *before*, on an average, the *before* must have been larger. We conclude that there is a significant reduction in blood pressure.

(41)

Home screen calculations are similar to those described in Topic 41.

Topic 45 (38)—Testing Hypothesis of Two Population Proportions

Test whether there is a difference in the proportion of men and women in a population who agree with a certain public policy. Base your conclusion on the simple random sample below where x is the number out of the sample of size n that agree.

Women: x1 = 694   n1 = 936

Men: x2 = 645   n2 = 941

Test Ho: $p_1 = p_2$, or $(p_1 - p_2 = 0)$ Ha: $p_1 \neq p_2$ or $(p_1 - p_2 \neq 0)$

1. Press $\boxed{\text{STAT}}$ <TESTS> 6:2-PropZTest for screen 42.

2. Enter the correct values as in screen 42, highlight **Calculate** in the last row, and then press $\boxed{\text{ENTER}}$ for output screens 43.

With a p-value of **0.0073**, there is very strong evidence that a larger percentage of women than men agree with the public policy (note that the sample proportions are 74.1 to 68.5 percent).

The pooled proportion is **(694 + 645)/(936 + 941) = 0.713.**

$z = (0.741 - 0.685)/\sqrt{(0.713 * (1 - 0.713) * (1/936 + 1/941))} = 2.68.$

Note: n1 = 936 = 694 + 242 (both values greater than 5). n2 = 941 = 645 + 296 (both values greater than 5). Therefore, the normal approximation to the binomial can be used.

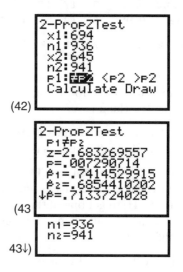

(42)

(43

43↓)

Topic 46—Testing Hypotheses of Standard Deviations of Two Normal Populations

To test if there is any difference in the variability of the diastolic blood pressure of men or women, a random sample of each was taken and recorded below.

| Male | (LMBP): | 76 | 74 | 70 | 80 | 68 | 90 | 70 | 72 | 76 | 68 | 96 |

| Female | (LFBP): | 70 | 82 | 90 | 68 | 60 | 62 | 80 | 74 | 62 |

	mean	Sx	n
Male	76.36	9.11	11
Female	72	10.34	9

Assuming that the populations of diastolic blood pressure are normally distributed, test:

H_0: $\sigma_1 = \sigma_2$ or $(\sigma_1^2/\sigma_2^2 = 1)$ H_a: $\sigma_1 \neq \sigma_2$ or $(\sigma_1^2/\sigma_2^2 \neq 1)$

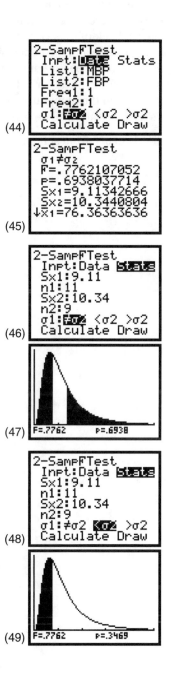

1. Store the male data stored in list **LMBP** and the female data in list **LFBP**.

2. Press STAT **<TESTS> D:2-SampFTest** for one of the two possible screens (see screens 44 and 46), depending on what input (**Inpt:**) is highlighted.

3. Enter the correct values as in screen 44 or 46, highlight **Calculate** or **Draw**, and then press ENTER.

    Screen 45 is the **Calculate** output for the **Data List** input of screen 44. Screen 47 is the **Draw** output for the **Stats** input of screen 46.

With a p-value of **0.6938**, we cannot reject the null hypothesis. The ratio of variances is not significantly different from 1, so there is no significant difference in the variability of male and female diastolic blood pressure.

The **F** above was calculated with $9.11^2/10.34^2 = 0.7762$.

Note that if there were a one-tailed test $(\sigma_1 < \sigma_2)$ (as in screen 48) with $\mathbf{F} = 9.11^2/10.34^2 = 0.7762$, we would see that the **p** value is half the value shown in screen 47, or that the p-value = **0.3469**, as in screen 49.

Before the existence of the TI-83, textbooks suggested that the largest sample variance (or standard deviation) be put in the numerator to force us to the right tail so it would be easier to use tables in back of these texts. You will see in screens 50 and 51 that the **p** value and the conclusion (from the textbooks' suggestions) would be the same as above; thus, it is no longer necessary to force the larger value into the numerator. If the larger value is in the numerator, the **F** ratio will be larger than 1; if it is not, the ratio will be less than 1.

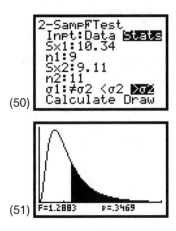

(50)

Note that 1/**1.2883** from screen 51 equals **0.7762** of screen 49.

(51)

Activity 9

Testing Goodness-of-Fit and Two-Way Table Chi-Square

Topic 47 tests to see if data follows a hypothesized distribution. Topic 48 builds on the descriptive two-way table analysis in Topic 18 to see if there is a significant relationship between two categorical variables.

Topic 47—Chi-Square Goodness-of-Fit Test

Uniform Distribution (Check on [MATH] <PRB>1:rand)

In Topic 26 (screen 56), you generated 100 random values between 0 and 10 and constructed a **Histogram** with ten classes of length 1. If the random generator was working effectively, we would expect ten values in each class. The observed and the expected values are given below. (Expected values are all greater than 5.)

Class	1	2	3	4	5	6	7	8	9	10
Observed (L$_1$)	9	10	7	15	14	5	14	8	10	8
Expected (L$_2$)	10	10	10	10	10	10	10	10	10	10

Test the hypothesis that the data comes from a uniform distribution:

1. With the observed values in **L₁** and the expected values in **L₂**, calculate [(] [2nd] **L₁** [−] [2nd] **L₂** [)] x^2 [÷] [2nd] **L₂** [STO▸] **L₃**, as in the first two lines shown in screen 1. Notice that the smallest and largest values are **0** and **2.5**; **0** to go with 10 (what we expected) and **2.5** to go with the biggest miss of 15.

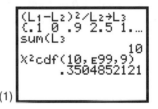

(1)

2. Press [2nd] [LIST] <MATH> **5:sum(** **L₃** [ENTER] for the chi-square statistic of 10. This is a one-tail test in that we are only concerned if the calculated chi-square is larger than we would expect for a uniform distribution. Degrees of freedom = 10 - 1 = 9.

3. Press [2nd] [DISTR] **7:χ²cdf(** **10** [,] [2nd] [EE] **99** [,] **9** [)] [ENTER] for a **p** value = **0.35**. (See the last line of screen 1.)

Note: Getting a statistic of 10 is a coincidence. If you generated another sample, the results would be different. All possible results would be approximately chi-square distributed.

A chi-square value of 10 is not that unusual for the sampling done at the beginning of this topic, so there is insufficient evidence for us to reject the hypothesis that the data came from a uniform distribution.

Binomial Distribution (Check on MATH <PRB>7:randBin)

In Topic 25 (screen 45), **randBin** was used to simulate 100 binomial experiments with **n = 10** and **p = 0.67**. The **Histogram** plotted gave the following observed frequencies:

X (L1):	0	1	2	3	4	5	6	7	8	9	10
Observed (L2):	0	0	0	2	3	12	23	26	24	10	0

Test the hypothesis that the data came from a binomial distribution with **n = 10** and **p = 0.67**.

With the random variable X (the number of successes) in **L1** and the observed frequency of each number of successes in **L2**, store the theoretical probabilities in **L3** by pressing [2nd] [DISTR] **0:binompdf(10 , 0 . 67** [STO►] **L3**, as shown in screen 2. Note that the probability of no successes is very small (**0.0000153**), so it does not surprise us when none of our 100 simulations produced ten failures (no successes).

Because there were 100 experiments, the theoretical frequencies are just 100 times the probabilities. These are stored in **L3** (shown in the last two lines in screen 2) for the results shown in screen 3. The first four rows have small expected frequencies, so we add them to the fifth row to get **7.32**, as shown in screen 4. (Many texts request the expected values be greater than 5 to assure the validity of the chi-square test.) The eleventh row had only 1.823 in it, so it was added to the 8.798 in the tenth row for 10.801. (See screen 4.) These additions must also be made in **L2**, so the first value will be $0 + 0 + 0 + 2 + 3 = 5$ and the last value $10 + 0 = 10$.

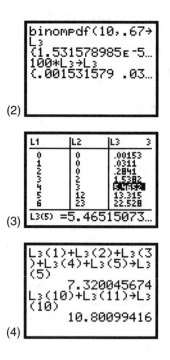

(2)

(3)

(4)

The results of the condensing on the previous page (with the help of the [DEL] key) are shown in screen 5, with the first row now representing four or fewer successes and the last row nine or ten successes. Note that the observed values in **L2** are fairly close to the expected values in **L3**.

Calculating the chi-square statistic (**1.78**), as shown in screen 6, we see that each contribution is small. Degrees of freedom = 6 - 1 = 5 because we reduced the number of cells to six by condensing.

The p-value of **0.879** (as on the last line in screen 6) indicates that our results are about what one would expect from the binomial distribution we hypothesized, so we certainly could not reject that hypothesis.

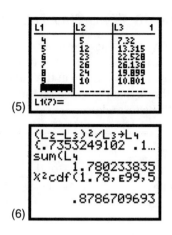

(5)

(6)

Topic 48—Two-Way Table Chi-Square Test

There was some concern that the wording of an exam was biased in favor of one sex. A random sample of the results for 263 test-takers is given in the table below. Test the null hypothesis that the grade on the exam is independent of the sex of the test-taker.

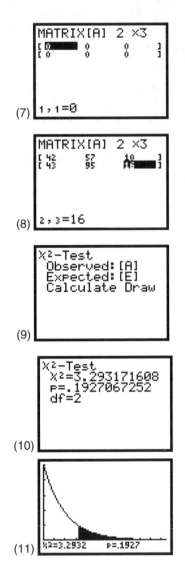

	Grade			
	Good	**Fair**	**Poor**	**Total**
Male	42	57	10	109
Female	43	95	16	154
Total				263

Storing Data in a Matrix

1. Press MATRX **<EDIT> 1: [A]** 2 ENTER 3 ENTER to display screen 7 with two rows and three columns. You may have values other than 0 in your matrix, but do not bother to change them because you will enter values over them.

2. Type **42** ENTER **57** ENTER **10** ENTER **43** ENTER **95** ENTER **16** ENTER to display screen 8. You can use the cursor control keys to edit any mistakes.

χ² Test

1. Press STAT **<TESTS> C: χ²-Test** to display screen 9.

2. Paste **[A]** and **[E]** from MATRX **<NAMES> 1** and **5**.

3. Highlight **Calculate** or **Draw**, and press ENTER for screens 10 or 11.

With a large p-value of **0.1927**, there is insufficient evidence to reject the null hypothesis. If there were no relationship between grade and sex, it is not unusual to get this kind of result.

*Note: If the sample size were twice as large and if the proportion in each cell the same (84 males and 86 females with good grades, and so on), this relationship would be significant with a **p** value of **0.037** (with males getting a significantly larger proportion of good grades than females and a significantly smaller proportion of fair grades—as you will see in the following section). Of course with a larger sample, the proportions could change.*

Expected Values

The expected values were calculated and stored in [E] and are shown in screen 12 with the original observed values in screen 13. Note that all expected values are greater than 5.

Some of the largest differences between observed and expected values are seen in the first column for those with the highest grades. If there were no relationship between grade and sex, we would expect about 35 good grades for the males. We had more than expected with 42. Because there were more females, we would expect more to receive good grades (about 50), but there were only 43. These differences are reasonable variations.

1. Transfer the data from matrix [A] to list L1, L2, and L3. You can do this by hand or by using 2nd [LIST] <OPS> A: Matr▸list([A] 、 L1 、 L2、 L3) ENTER for **DONE**.

2. Add the column totals into row 3 and the row totals into column **L4** by hand or as explained on the first page of Topic 18.

    The results are shown in screens 14 and 15.

    As an example of how to calculate expected values from the spreadsheet, in step 3, we will calculate the second column of expected values on the home screen.

3. Proceed as shown in screen 16 by multiplying the sum of the first row times the sum of the second column and dividing by the grand total in **L4(3)** for **62.996**, and so on. Note that these agree with the values stored in matrix [E].

Percents and Bar Charts

If you calculate the row percentages as done in Topic 18 and in screens 17 and 18, you see that 38.5 percent of males and 27.9 percent of females made good grades (32.3 percent of the sample total of 263 test-takers made good grades). These differences were not significant for this sample size. These percentages could be put in bar charts as you did in Topic 18.

χ^2 Contributions

If matrix [A] were transferred to L1, L2, and L3 and matrix [E] to L4, L5, and L6, then the χ^2 contributions could be calculated, as in screen 19, with the results shown in screen 20. The sum of all these values is the **3.293** of the χ^2-**TEST** output. Notice that most of the contributions come from **L1** (good grades).

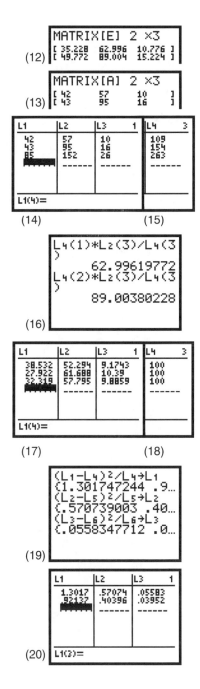

E X P L O R A T I O N S

Activity 10

Analyzing Variance (ANOVA)

Topic 49 uses STAT <TESTS> **F:ANOVA** with lists of data gathered from a completely randomized design. Program **A1ANOVA** (see *Appendix B*) is introduced with its capability of using summary statistics for input. Program **A1ANOVA** can also use raw data stored in a matrix as opposed to a list. This technique is required for those who will analyze randomized block designs and two-factor factorial experiments, which are presented in Topics 50 and 51.

The idea for the examples used in this chapter is from McClave/Benson, STATISTICS FOR BUSINESS AND ECONOMICS, 5/e, ©1992, pp. 870, 891, 909. Reprinted by permission of Prentice Hall, Upper Saddle River, New Jersey.

Topic 49—Completely Randomized Designs (One-Way ANOVA)

To compare the distances traveled by three different brands of golf balls when struck by a driver, we use a completely randomized design. A robotic golfer, using a driver, is set up to hit a random sample of 24 balls (8 of each brand) in a random sequence. The distance is recorded for each hit, and the results are shown in the table below, organized by brand.

	L1	L2	L3
Brand	Brand A	Brand B	Brand C
Distance	264.3	262.9	241.9
	258.6	259.9	238.6
	266.4	264.7	244.9
	256.5	254	236.2
	182.7	191.2	167.3
	181	189	165.9
	177.6	185.5	162.4
	187.3	192.1	172.5
Mean	221.8	224.9	203.7
StdDev	42.58	38.08	39.4
n	8	8	8

Activity 10, Analyzing Variance (ANOVA) (cont.)

Test the null hypothesis H_0: $\mu_A = \mu_B = \mu_C$.

1. With the data stored in lists **L1**, **L2**, and **L3**, press [STAT] <TESTS> F:ANOVA(**L1** [,] **L2** [,] **L3**, as shown in screen 1.

2. Press [ENTER] to display the next two screens (2 and 3).

With the p-value of **0.531**, the data shows no significant difference between the mean distance traveled by the three brands of balls. We do not reject the null hypothesis.

Bonferroni Multiple Comparison Procedure

Since we do not reject the null hypothesis, there is no significant difference between any of the means. A multiple comparison procedure is not needed or appropriate.

Topic 50 gives an example of the multiple comparison procedure that relates back to this topic, so you will know how to proceed if the null hypothesis above is rejected.

Program A1ANOVA

Program **A1ANOVA** is available from Texas Instruments over the internet (**www.ti.com**) or on disk (**1-800-TI-CARES**) and can be transferred to your TI-83 using TI-GRAPH LINK™. (The program listing is in Appendix B.)

1. Press [PRGM], highlight program **A1ANOVA**, and then press [ENTER] to paste the name, as shown in screen 4.

2. Press [ENTER] for the menu on screen 5.

3. Press **1:ONE-WAY ANOVA** for screen 6, which informs you of two options for input of the data: a matrix or summary statistics. The procedures for using these options follow.

Using Summary Statistics

1. Press [ENTER], and the menu (screen 7) presents the options mentioned in screen 6.

2. Select **2:x̄1,Sx1,n1,x̄2** for screen 8.

3. When prompted with **HOW MANY LEVELS?** (screen 8) type **3**, and then press [ENTER]. (There are three levels or brands.)

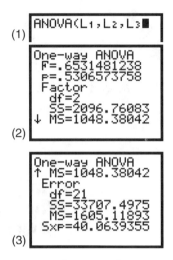

(1)

(2)

(3)

Note: $Sxp = \sqrt{(MSE)} = \sqrt{(1605.11893)} = 40.0639355$. (See screen 3.)

(4)

(5)

(6)

(7)

(8)

4. Enter the means, standard deviations, and sample sizes for each level, as shown in screens 8 and 9. After you press ENTER the final time, the **ANOVA** table appears (screen 10).

The results are basically the same as before. The differences occur because the means and standard deviations were rounded with the summary statistics.

The mean squares, MS, are not given in the table but are easily calculated with MS = **SS/DF** or, for **Factor**: **2097.76**/2 = 1048.9 and for **Error**: **33708.52**/21 = 1605.2.

5. Press ENTER again, and 95 percent confidence intervals (screen 11) for each mean are calculated based on the pooled standard deviation **SP** or **Sxp**.

Note all of these intervals overlap, indicating there is no significant difference between the means.

Using Matrix [D]

1. Enter the 24 data values in a 24x2 matrix [D] (see screen 12) with all the distance data in column 1 and the level or brand data in column 2 (eight 1s, eight 2s, and eight 3s).

This is explained in the informational screen (screen 6) that appears after you select **ONE-WAY ANOVA**. (See "Storing Data in a Matrix" in Topic 48. You may enter data by column by pressing ▼ after each value instead of ENTER as shown in Topic 48.)

2. Select **1:DATA MAT [D]**, as shown in screen 13.

The **ANOVA** table appears. (See screen 14.)

Press ENTER again to get the sample size, means, and standard deviations for the three levels. (See screen 15. Use ▶ to view the standard deviation.)

3. Press ENTER for the confidence intervals, which are the same as above. (See screen 11.)

If you wonder how a robot swinging a driver could get such wide variations in distances, several possible explanations exist:
- The wind was shifting and gusting.
- The balls were inconsistently made.
- The robot hit with a wide variability of forces.

Other reasons are given in the next two topics.

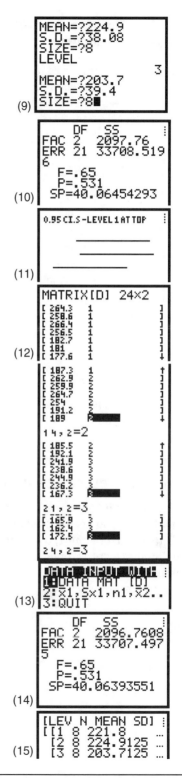

(9)

(10)

(11)

(12)

(13)

(14)

(15)

Topic 50—Randomized Block Design (Program A1ANOVA)

Suppose eight golfers are randomly selected and each golfer hits three balls, one of each brand, in a random sequence. The distance is measured and recorded, as shown in the table below and in matrix [D] on the TI-83. (See screen 16.)

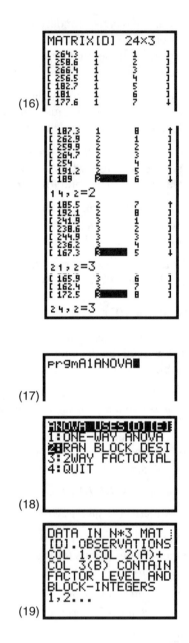

(16)

Golfer (Block)	Brand A	Brand B	Brand C
1	264.3	262.9	241.9
2	258.6	259.9	238.6
3	266.4	264.7	244.9
4	256.5	254	236.2
5	182.7	191.2	167.3
6	181	189	165.9
7	177.6	185.5	162.4
8	187.3	192.1	172.5
Mean	221.8	224.9	203.7
StdDev	42.58	38.08	39.4
n	8	8	8

Test the null hypothesis H_0: $\mu_A = \mu_B = \mu_C$.

1. Press PRGM, highlight program **A1ANOVA**, and then press ENTER so the name is pasted, as shown in screen 17.

    (17)

2. Press ENTER for the menu in screen 18.

3. Press **2:RAN BLOCK DESIGN** for screen 19.

    This screen informs you how to input the data into matrix [D]. You need a 24x3 matrix with the 24 distances in column 1, the factor levels (brands) in column 2 (eight 1s, eight 2s, and eight 3s), and the block integer (golfer) in column 3 (1 to 8 three times). See the matrix example in screen 16.

    (18)

    (19)

4. Press [ENTER], and then "continue" for the **ANOVA** table shown in screen 20.

   The very large F-value of **168.24** and a p-value of 0 to 3 decimal places (**0.000**) leads us to reject the null hypothesis and conclude that the mean distances are not all the same for the three brands of balls.

5. Press [ENTER] to see screen 21.

   Screen 21 shows **S** = $\sqrt{MSE}$ = $\sqrt{SS/DF}$ = $\sqrt{87.2392/14}$ = **2.49627**.

```
         DF   SS
 A    2   2096.76083
 B    7   33620.2583
 ER  14   87.2391667

      F(A)=168.24
         P=0.000
      F(B)=770.76
```
(20)

```
 B         P=0.000


         S=2.496271029
```
(21)

Bonferroni Multiple Comparison Procedure

We will use the Bonferroni Procedure to see which means differ. The table below shows the means ranked in order. (Note that the **ONE-WAY ANOVA** option of program **A1ANOVA** could be run with the current matrix [D] and used to find the means for each brand of ball.)

Brand:	C	A	B
Mean:	203.7	221.8	224.9

Number of Pairwise Comparisons: C = k(k – 1)/2

There are three **nCr 2** ways of picking pairs from three means or $3 * 2/2 = 3$ (with **nCr** under [MATH] <PRB>). These are CA, CB, and AB. Note that if there were four means, this would be four **nCr 2** = $4 * 3/2 = 6$ pairs.

Comparisonwise Significance Level ÷ 2: α /(2C)

In doing multiple t-tests of H_0: $\mu_1 = \mu_2$ with the alternate H_a: $\mu_1 \neq \mu_2$, and holding the overall experimental significance level to $\alpha = 0.05$, you will need to use a comparisonwise significance level = 0.05/3. Because you are doing a two-tail test, you must divide this by 2 for 0.05/6 = 0.00833 in each tail.

Critical *t*-value

With **0.00833** in the right tail of a t-distribution with 14 degrees of freedom (**Error** degrees of freedom), use the MATH equation solver to solve **tcdf(X, E99, 14) = 0.00833** for **x**, as explained on the last page of Topic 34. **X** is the critical value and equals **2.718**, as verified with [2nd] [DISTR] **5:tcdf(** 2 [.] **718** [,] **E99** [,] **14** [ENTER], for an area of **0.00833**, as shown in screen 22.

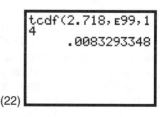

```
tcdf(2.718,E99,1
4
        .0083293348
```
(22)

Comparisons

Calculate $t = (\bar{x}2 - \bar{x}1) \div (\sqrt{(MSE)} * \sqrt{(1/n1 + 1/n2)})$ for each comparison.

For **AC**:
$t = (221.8 - 203.7) \div (2.49627 * \sqrt{(1/8 + 1/8)}) = 14.502 > 2.718$

For **BC**:
$t = (224.9 - 203.7) \div (2.49627 * \sqrt{(1/8 + 1/8)}) = 16.985 > 2.718$

For **AB**:
$t = (224.9 - 221.8) \div (2.49627 * \sqrt{(1/8 + 1/8)}) = 2.484 < 2.718$

The 2nd [ENTRY] feature is helpful for doing the previous calculations on the home screen, as shown in screen 23.

Notice that Brand C has a smaller mean distance than either Brand A or Brand B, but brands A and B do not have significantly different means. We show this with a line over or under A and B, but not C:

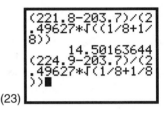

(23)

$$C\,A\,B \text{ or } C\,\underline{A}\,\underline{B}$$

Bonferroni for Completely Randomized Designs (Topic 49)

In Topic 49, we did not do the multiple comparisons procedure with the example because there was no significant difference between any of the means. If we could have rejected the null hypothesis, then we would have done the Bonferroni Procedure as it was done above. The means were the same but $S = \sqrt{MSE} = 40.0639$ and the **Error** degree of freedom was 21 (which leads to a critical t-value of 2.601). The largest difference is between Brand B and Brand C for the following t statistic:
$$t = (224.9 - 203.7) \div (40.0639 * \sqrt{(1/8 + 1/8)}) = 1.0583 < 2.601$$

There is, therefore, no significant difference.

Note that for the completely randomized designs, the sample sizes do not have to be of the same size ($n1 \neq n2$).

Although the data is the same, there is a large difference in the MSE in Topics 49 and 50. Because of the different power in which different golfers could hit the ball, we were able to block out much of the variability in Topic 50. All golfers were not able to hit Brand C as far as the other two brands. There was no such blocking possible in Topic 49, where the variability was due to other unknown causes. Although the means were the same in the two cases, there was no significant difference in Topic 49. If the null hypothesis were true, it is quite possible that another sample of 24 balls would have Brand C with the greater mean distance, but not significantly different from the other two brands.

Topic 51—Two-Factor Designs With Equal Replicates

Suppose we test three brands of golf balls and two different clubs (driver and five-iron) in a completely randomized design. Each of the six ball-club combinations is randomly and independently assigned to four experimental units, each of which consists of a specific position in the sequence of hits by a golf robot. The distance response is recorded for each of the 24 hits, and the results are shown in the table below and in the matrix [D] shown in screen 24.

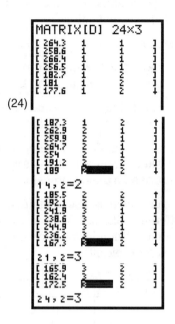

(24)

Factor B	Factor A		
(Club)	Brand A	Brand B	Brand C
Driver	264.3	262.9	241.9
	258.6	259.9	238.6
	266.4	264.7	244.9
	256.5	254	236.2
Five-iron	182.7	191.2	167.3
	181	189	165.9
	177.6	185.5	162.4
	187.3	192.1	172.5

The data is stored in matrix [D] of order 24x3 with the distance data in column 1, Factor-A level in column 2 (**1**, **2** or **3** for Brand A, B, or C) and Factor-B level in column 3 (**1** for driver or **2** for five-iron). For example, the last value in the table above and in the last row of matrix [D] is **172.5**, which is the distance a Brand C (**3**) ball is hit with a five-iron (**2**).

1. Press [PRGM], highlight program **A1ANOVA**, and then press [ENTER] so the name is pasted, as shown in screen 25.

2. Press [ENTER] for the menu on screen 26.

3. Press **3:2WAY FACTORIAL** for screen 27, which informs you how to input the data into matrix [D] as was done above.

4. Press [ENTER] and then 'continue' for the **ANOVA** table at the top of the next page.

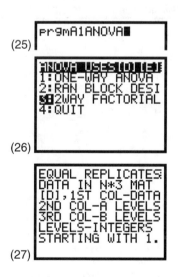

(25)

(26)

(27)

We see from the results that there is no significant interaction with $F(AB)$ = **2.21** and a p-value = **0.139**. This is also clear from the **xyLine** plots (screen 30) of the mean for each of the six ball-club combinations recorded in the table below.

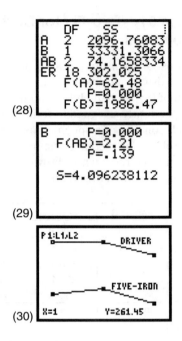

(28)

(29)

(30)

The plots are obtained as follows.

1. Store **1, 2, 3** in L_1, the three driver means in L_2, and the three five-iron means in L_3.

2. Set up **Plot1** (for L_1 and L_2) and **Plot2** (for L_1 and L_3) as **xyLine** plots (see in Topic 1).

There is a significant difference between the B factors (p-value = **0.000**). It is clear that the driver drives the ball further on average than the five-iron, just as we would expect.

Because there is also a significant difference between the different balls (Factor A), Brand C seems least effective for distance. Multiple comparisons could also be done similar to those in Topic 50.

Factor B	Factor A (L_1)		
(Club)	Brand A	Brand B	Brand C
	(1)	(2)	(3)
Driver (L_2)	261.45	260.38	240.4
Five-iron (L_3)	182.15	189.45	167.03

Activity 11

Inference for Correlation and Regression

Both the introduction and Topic 11 in Activity 3 discussed fitting a straight line to bivariate data. Topic 52 below extends this discussion to test if a significant relationship exists between the two variables and then calculate the confidence and predictive intervals.

Topic 53 extends the above to more than one independent variable and explains how to use program **A2MULREG**, which also automates the procedure in Topic 52.

Topic 52—Simple Linear Regression and Correlation (Hypothesis Test and Confidence and Predictive Intervals)

A study was conducted to investigate if there was a relationship between the length of time a student studies outside of class each week and the final grade in a course. A simple random sample of ten students from the course was used and is given below.

Student	1	2	3	4	5	6	7	8	9	10
Hrs. Studied (x) L1:	3.5	6	7	3	4.5	7.5	4	6.5	5.5	5
Final Grade (y) L2:	75	95	83	69	77	93	73	87	78	86

Put hours in list **L1** and grades in **L2**, and then continue with the following procedure.

Activity 11, Inference for Correlation and Regression (cont.)

1. Set up a **scatter** plot.

   Set up **Plot1** as in Topic 7, and press [ZOOM] 9:**ZoomStat** [TRACE] for screen 1. The ◄ ► keys can be used to highlight each point.

2. Test the null hypothesis H₀: β = 0 and H₀: ρ = 0.

   a. Press [STAT] <TESTS>E:**LinRegTTest** for screen 2.

   b. Paste **L1** and **L2** for the **Xlist** and **Ylist** and paste **Y1** for the **RegEQ** with [VARS] <Y-VARS>1:**Function** 1:**Y1**.

   Note the alternate hypothesis is set at β ≠ 0 and ρ ≠ 0.

   c. Highlight **Calculate** at the bottom of screen 2 and press [ENTER] for the first screens 3 and 4, where:

   regression line = y = a + bx = **56.90909 + 4.70303**x
   correlation coefficient = r = **0.82491**
   coefficient of determination = r2 = **0.68048**

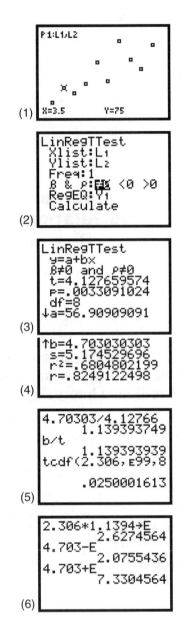

(1) X=3.5   Y=75

(2)
```
LinRegTTest
Xlist:L1
Ylist:L2
Freq:1
β & ρ:≠0 <0 >0
RegEQ:Y1
Calculate
```

(3)
```
LinRegTTest
y=a+bx
β≠0 and ρ≠0
t=4.127659574
p=.0033091024
df=8
↓a=56.90909091
```

(4)
```
↑b=4.703030303
s=5.174529696
r²=.6804802199
r=.8249122498
```

(5)
```
4.70303/4.12766
          1.139393749
b/t
          1.139393939
tcdf(2.306,E99,8)
          .0250001613
```

(6)
```
2.306*1.1394→E
          2.6274564
4.703-E
          2.0755436
4.703+E
          7.3304564
```

With a p-value of **0.003309** and **b** and **r** positive, we conclude that the slope of the population regression line β is significantly different from zero and that there is significant positive correlation between hours studied and final grade.

3. Find 95 percent confidence interval for β.

   t = (b − 0)/S$_b$; therefore, S$_b$ = b/t = **4.70303/4.12766** = **1.1394**, as shown in screen 5. Notice you could paste **b** and **t** with [VARS] 5:**Statistics.**<EQ> 3:**b** and [VARS] 5:**Statistics.**<TEST> 3:**t**.

   a. Find the critical t-value from a table or by using the equation solver to solve **tcdf(X, E99, 8) = 0.025** for **X**, as explained at the end of Topic 34. (Degrees of freedom = n − 2 = 10 − 2 = 8.)

   b. To verify the critical value X = **2.306**, press [2nd] [DISTR] 5:**tcdf(2.306** , **E99** , **8**) [ENTER] for **0.025** (see the last two lines in screen 5).

   The margin of error is **t** ∗ **S$_b$** = **2.627** = **E**, as shown in the first lines of screen 6.

We are 95 percent confident that the slope of the population regression line is between 2.08 and 7.33. For each additional hour that a student studies, we expect the grade to increase from between 2.08 to 7.33 percentage points.

4. Plot data and regression line with point estimates when $X = 3.5$.

   a. With **Plot1** still set up from step 1 and with the regression equation automatically stored in **Y₁** from step 2, press [TRACE] [▲] for the graph in screen 7. The cursor is flashing on the regression line.

   b. Press [◄] until you are close to **3.5** (**3.5266** is the closest pixel (screen 8)).

   c. Type **3.5** and the large **X=3.5** appears at the bottom of the screen (screen 9).

      Press [ENTER] for **Y= 73.369697** (screen 10).

      You also could have entered **3.5** into the regression equation, as shown in screen 11.

(7)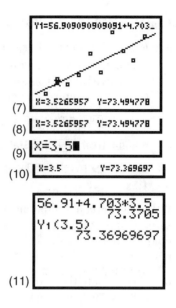

(8)

(9)

(10)

(11)

5. Calculate residuals and residual plots.

   Because all the points do not fall on the regression line, an interval estimate makes more sense than the point estimate used in step 4. A measure of the difference between the actual y-value of the data and the y-value on the regression curve for the same **x** is called the *residual*. (For the first point, **x = 3.5** and **y =75**, the regression line gives **Y₁(3.5) = 73.3697**, so the residual is **75 - 73.3697 = 1.6303**.) The residuals for all the data points are automatically stored in list **LRESID** in step 2 (see the first two lines in screen 12).

   A measure of the scatter of the points about the regression line is the square root of the sum of the residual squared divided by (**n - 2**), or **s = 5.1745**, as shown in the last line of screen 12 and in screen 4.

(12)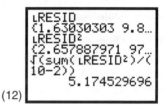

   a. Set up **Plot2** for a scatter plot with the Xlist = **L₁** and Ylist = **LRESID** and with all other stat plots and Y= plots turned off.

   b. Press [ZOOM] **9:ZoomStat** [TRACE] for the plot in screen 13.

      Notice a fairly random pattern, but the residuals seem to get larger for longer study times.

(13)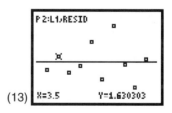

6. Find 95 percent predictive and confidence intervals.

   a. For **X = 3.5** and the critical t value, **T = 2.306** (as calculated in step 3), you can calculate the predictive interval, as shown in screens 14 and 15 (other **X**s or interval levels could be used):

      s from [VARS] **5:Statistics <TEST> 0:s.**

      n and $\bar{x}$ from [VARS] **5:Statistics <XY> 1:n** and **2:** $\bar{x}$.

      Σ**x²** and Σ**x** from [VARS] **5:Statistics <Σ> 2:Σx²** and **1:Σx.**

```
3.5→X:2.306→T:Y₁
(X)→Y
           73.36969697
T*s√(1+1/n+n(X-x̄
)²/(n*Σx²-(Σx)²)
)→E
           13.33281413
```
(14)

```
Y-E
           60.03688284
Y+E
           86.7025111
```
(15)

We are 95 percent confident (based on this small sample) that the grade obtained by a student who studies 3.5 hours a week is between about 60 and 87 percent.

   b. To calculate the confidence interval, use the [2nd] [ENTRY] feature to recall the lines, as in screen 16, and then delete the **1+** under the square root sign.

```
3.5→X:2.306→T:Y₁
(X)→Y
           73.36969697
T*s√(1/n+n(X-x̄)²
/(n*Σx²-(Σx)²))→
E
           5.94812577
```
(16)

      As shown in screen 17, we obtain approximately 67 to 79 percent.

```
Y-E
           67.4215712
Y+E
           79.31782274
```
(17)

The confidence interval is narrower than the predictive interval because this is the mean time we would predict for all students who study 3.5 hours (thus, by the *Central Limit Theorem*, the highs and the lows average out).

Topic 53 automates this process.

Topic 53—Multiple Regression and Program A2MULREG

To possibly improve the prediction capability of the regression equation developed in Topic 52 (which we will assume you are familiar), the age of the student (perhaps, related to motivation) will also be considered (see below).

Student	C1 Y (Grade)	C2 X1 (Study Hrs.)	C3 X2 (Age Yrs.)
1	75	3.5	20
2	95	6	19
3	83	7	36
4	69	3	21
5	77	4.5	27
6	93	7.5	24
7	73	4	22
8	87	6.5	34
9	78	5.5	23
10	86	5	25

Store the above data into a 10x3 matrix [D] as discussed in Topic 48 and partially shown in screen 18. The Y-values must be in column 1 (**C1**) of the matrix.

1. Set up program **A2MULREG**.

    Program **A2MULREG** is available from Texas Instruments over the internet (www.ti.com) or on disk (1-800-TI-CARES) and can be stored in your TI-83 with TI-GRAPH LINK. (The program listing is provided in Appendix B.)

    a. Press PRGM <EXEC>, highlight program **A2MULREG**, and then press ENTER to paste the name to the screen, as shown in screen 19.

    b. Press ENTER for the next screen (screen 20), which reminds you to put the data in matrix [D] and informs you that matrices [A] to [F] will be used by the program. To eliminate the fear of losing data, you can use matrices [G], [H], [I], and [J] for saving data.

    Notice the pause indicator in the upper right corner of the screen waiting for input or, in this case, for you to press ENTER.

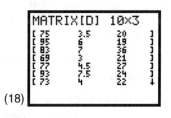

(18)

Note: *The first two columns above were stored in L2 and L1 in Topic 52 so they could be transferred to matrix [D] (as discussed in Topic 18) using* 2nd *[LIST] <OPS> 0:Listmatr(L2* , *L1* , *[D]* ENTER)*. This gives a 10 x 2 matrix. Change this to 10 x 3, and enter the last column by using* ▼.

(19) `prgmA2MULREG█`

(20)
```
DATA IN MAT [D]
COL Y,X1,X2,..XN
Y MUST BE IN THE
1ST COL OF [D].

[A],[B],[C],[D],
[E]+[F] USED.
```

2. Make the correlation matrix.

   a. Press [ENTER] for the menu in screen 21, and select **2:CORR MATRIX** for screen 22.

   b. View the rest of the matrix by pressing [▶].

   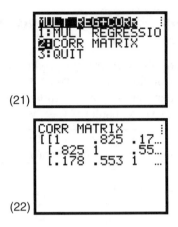

   (21)

   The simple linear correlation coefficient between **Y** and **X1** is **0.825** (as in Topic 52), between **Y** and **X2** is **0.178**, and between **X1** and **X2** is **0.553**.

   Again, notice the pause indicator. Pressing [ENTER] gives a **Done**.

3. Calculate simple linear regression. (**Y = B0 + B1 x 1**)

   (22)

   To relate program **A2MULREG** to Topic 52, we will use only the first two columns of matrix [D]. The matrix could have been of order 10x2, but 10x3 is also acceptable because the last column is ignored for this step.

   *Note: If no calculations have been done on the home screen since program **A2MULREG** was last run, pressing [ENTER] will restart the program.*

   a. Rerun program **A2MULREG**, and select **1:MULT REGRESSION** from the menu screen (screen 21) for screen 23.

   b. Enter **1** for **HOW MANY IND**ependent **VAR**iables, and then press [ENTER].

   (23)

   c. Enter **2** for **COL**umn of independent **VAR**iable. Remember **Y** is in column 1 and **X1** is in column 2.

   (24)

   Because there is only one independent variable, you have the option of automatically plotting the scatter of points with the least square regression line, as shown in screen 26 and in Topic 52 (screens 1 and 7).

   (25)

   d. Press [ENTER].

   After a brief wait while the busy indicator is on in the upper right corner of the screen, the output in screen 27 appears, and the indicator changes to pause.

   (26)

   p-value = **0.003**, r^2 = **0.6805** = **R-SQ**, s = **5.1745** and $\sqrt{F} = \sqrt{(17.04)} = 4.13 = t$, all as in Topic 52. (Screens 3 and 4)

   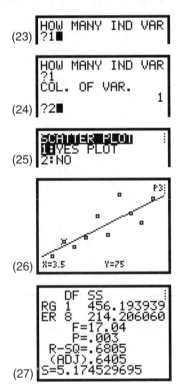

   F = (**456.193939/1**)/(**214.206060/8**)

   = (**456.193939**)/(**26.7757575**) = **17.04**

   (27)

   with MSR = **456.193939** and MSE = **26.7757575**.

e. Press [ENTER] and the output is completed with
    B0 = a = **56.9091**.

    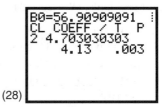
    (28)

    The **COEFF**icient of the **Co**Lumn 2 is **B1** = b =
    4.70303. Therefore, the regression equation is **Y** =
    56.9091 + **4.70303**x, as in Topic 52 (screens 3 and 4).
    The **t** and **p** are given in the last line in screen 28.

    The **t** of **4.13** is under the coefficient used to test the
    hypothesis $\beta 1 = 0$. The **p** value of **0.003** is beside the
    t-value it goes with.

    In the simple linear regression case, the t-value and
    the F-value are directly related because there is
    only one independent variable. In the multiple
    regression case, there are multiple t -values and
    none are directly related to the F-value.

4. Find confidence and predictive intervals.
    (**Y** = **B0** + **B1** x **1**)

    a. After finding the simple linear regression, press
        [ENTER].

        This reveals the MAIN MENU in screen 29 for the
        Multiple Regression option of program **A2MULREG**.

    b. Select **1:CONF+PRI INTER** for input screen 30.

        Enter **2.306** for the critical value for 95 percent
        intervals with 8 degrees of freedom (10 - 2 = 8), as
        in Topic 52 (screen 5).

    c. Press [ENTER], and type **3.5** for the number of hours
        studied for which you want to predict the final
        grade earned (screen 31).

    d. Press [ENTER] again to reveal the confidence interval,
        the predictive interval, and the point estimate **73.37**
        percent; all as in Topic 52 (screens 14-17), but this
        time, automated (screen 32).

        Pressing [ENTER] again gives you the option of either
        entering another **X** or returning to the MAIN MENU.

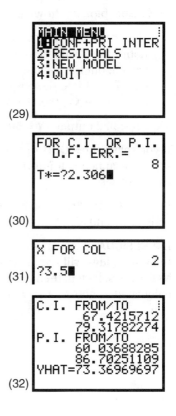
(29)

(30)

(31)

(32)

5. Plot residuals. (**Y = B0 + B1 x 1**)

   a. From the **MAIN MENU**, select **2:RESIDUALS** for the menu in screen 33, which provides the option of plotting the residuals, plotting the standard residuals, or calculating the Durbin-Watson statistic.

   b. Select **1:RESIDUAL PLOT** for the next option (screen 34).

   c. Select **2 VS AN IND VAR** for the prompt "**WHAT COL?**". Enter **2** at this prompt for **X2**. The same residual plot appears as shown in screen 13 in Topic 52.

   d. Press ENTER and repeat the process for **1 VS YHAT** for the plot, as shown in screen 35.

   Notice the plot has the same scatter of points. Also, notice the Y-values are the same as the previous screen, but the X-values are now the result of entering **X1** into the regression equation (**YHAT**s) and not the **X1**s themselves.

6. View residual output. (**Y = B0 + B1 x 1**)

   If you select the **5:QUIT** option after pressing ENTER, screen 36 appears. It informs you where certain values can be observed.

   Press **STAT 1:Edit** for the first six lists, as shown in screens 37 and 38.

   If **2:RESIDUALS** is *not* selected from the MAIN MENU, then the values will *not* be listed as above. If **3:NEW MODEL** is selected, then even if the values had been calculated as above, they would now be cleared for the new model.

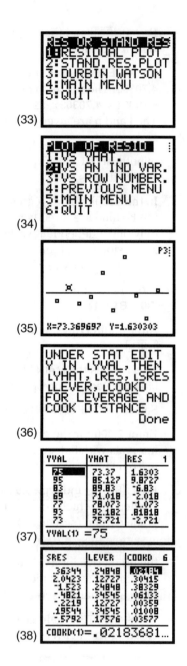

(33)

(34)

(35)

(36)

(37)

(38)

7. Calculate multiple regression. ($Y = B0 + B1 x 1 + B2 x 2$)

If you have selected **3:NEW MODEL** from the MAIN MENU or **1:MULT REGRESSION** after starting program **A2MULREG**, you will get a series of input screens like those condensed in screen 39.

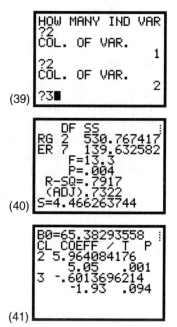

(39)

a. Select two independent variables with **X1** in column 2 and **X2** in column 3 of matrix [D].

b. Press ENTER for screen 40, which shows very significant overall regression with a **p** value of **0.004**. **R-SQ** has been increased to **0.7917** from **0.6805** with only **X1** in the model and **s** decreased to **4.466** from **5.1745**.

(40)

c. Press ENTER again for screen 41 with the regression equation **Y = 65.3829 + 5.9641X1 - 0.6014X2**.

Testing H0: $\beta1 = 0$ against $\beta1 \neq 0$ brings a **t = 5.05** with a **p** value = **0.001**.

Testing H0: $\beta2 = 0$ against $\beta2 \neq 0$ brings a **t = -1.93** with a **p** value = **0.094**.

(41)

Note: Age (X2) does not add significantly to the model (at a = 0.05 < 0.094).

8. Find confidence and predictive intervals. ($Y = B0 + B1 x 1 + B2 x 2$)

a. After completing step 7 for multiple regression, press ENTER to reveal the MAIN MENU for the **Multiple Regression** option of program **A2MULREG** (see screen 42).

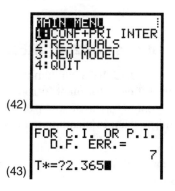

(42)

b. Select **1:CONF+PRI INTER** for the input shown in screen 43.

Enter **2.365** for the critical value for 95 percent intervals with degrees of freedom = 10 - 3 = 7 from a table or as done in Topic 35 with the equation solver.

(43)

c. Press [ENTER], and then type **3.5** for **X1** (in **COL 2**), the number of hours studied weekly by the student of interest (screen 44).

d. Press [ENTER], and then type **25** for **X2** (in **COL 3**), the age of the student of interest (screen 44).

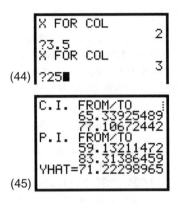

(44)

e. Press [ENTER] again to reveal the confidence interval, the predictive interval, and the point estimate of **71** percent (screen 45) compared to the point estimate of 73 percent without age in the model. The interval widths also decreased a bit.

(45)

Pressing [ENTER] again now gives you the option of entering another **X** or returning to the MAIN MENU (screen 42).

9. Plot residuals.

a. From the MAIN MENU, press **2:RESIDUALS** for the menu in screen 33.

b. Select **1:RESIDUAL PLOT** for the options in screen 34, and select **1 VS YHAT** for the plot shown in screen 46.

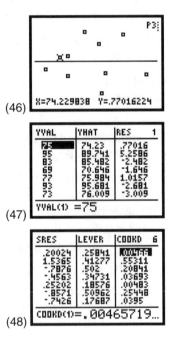

(46)

If you now press [2nd] [QUIT], the residual output is entered in the stat editor, as shown in screens 47 and 48.

(47)

Limitations of A2MULREG

Program **A2MULREG** can handle many variables and data points sufficient for most Introductory Statistics text data sets, but is limited by the memory of the TI-83. For large data sets, you might want to clear some items saved in memory.

(48)

Remember, the columns of a matrix and a list can be interchanged (as in Topic 18), making data transformations possible.

EXPLORATIONS

Activity 12

Forecasting Making forecasts from data requires many tools, including regression that was covered in Activity 11. In Activity 12, we will look at two techniques: Topic 54 covers *exponential smoothing* using some of the spreadsheet capabilities of the TI-83. Topic 55 covers program **FORECAST**, which uses a multiplicative time-series model with trend, seasonal, and irregular components.

The data for this activity is given below along with a plot in screen 1. The data represents the number of customers for a small business over the past four years.

		x in **L1**	y in **L2**
Year	Quarer	Period	Count
1	1	1	593
	2	2	512
	3	3	705
	4	4	756
2	1	5	680
	2	6	623
	3	7	785
	4	8	846
3	1	9	708
	2	10	662
	3	11	853
	4	12	884
4	1	13	736
	2	14	692
	3	15	908
	4	16	945

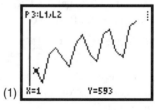

(1)

Put the time period in list **L1** and the customer count in **L2**, and then continue with Activity 12.

Topic 54—Exponential Smoothing

We will use the model $F_{t+1} = \alpha Y_t + (1 - \alpha)F_t$. This model uses the data for this period (Y_t) and the forecast for this period (F_t) to forecast for the next period (F_{t+1}). α is the smoothing constant and can be a value from 0 to 1.

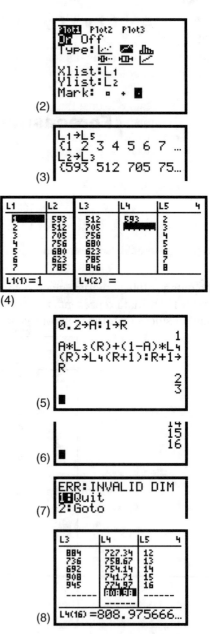

(2)

(3)

(4)

Setup

1. With the data in **L1** and **L2**, as depicted in the table at the beginning of Activity 12, set up **Plot1** for an **xyLine** plot, as shown in Topic 9 and in screen 2.

   Press [ZOOM] **9:ZoomStat** [TRACE] for the plot shown in screen 1.

2. Store a copy of **L1** in **L5** with **L1** [STO▸] **L5**, and store a copy of **L2** in **L3** (screen 3).

3. Press [STAT] **1:Edit** [DEL] to delete the first value of both **L3** and **L5**, and store the deleted value of **L3** in the first row of **L4**.

   The lists should look those in screen 4.

First Try ($\alpha = 0.2$)

1. Type **0** [.] **2** [STO▸] **A : 1** [STO▸] **R** (*do not* forget the colon) [ENTER] for the first two lines in screen 5.

2. Type **A** [×] **L3** [(] **R** [)] [+] [(] **1** [–] **A** [)] [×] **L4** [(] **R** [)] [STO▸] **L4** [(] **R** [+] **1** [)] **: R** [+] **1** [STO▸] **R**. Then press [ENTER] until you run out of data (about 16 times, one for each point) and get the error message **ERR:INVALID DIM**, as shown in screen 7.

3. Select **1:Quit**, and then press [STAT] **1:Edit**, and use the cursor control keys to go to the last value of **L4** for the forecast for the next period:

   F_{17} = 808.976 or 809 customers (screen 8).

4. Use [DEL] to delete the last value in **L4** so that **L3**, **L4**, and **L5** are all the same length (15 rows).

   Measures of Fit will use the 15 values in **L3** and **L4**. The first period value was dropped because it had no forecast, but was used as the forecast for the second period.

Note: If you get a dimension error in step 4, you forgot to delete the extra value in L4.

(5)

(6)

(7)

(8)

5. Use [2nd] [QUIT] to return to the home screen, and then press [2nd] [LIST] <MATH> 5:sum([(] L3 [−] L4 [)] [x²] [)] [÷] 15 [ENTER] for the first two lines in screen 9.

This is the *Mean of the Squared Errors*, or MSE = **14284.7**.

6. Press [2nd] [LIST] <MATH> 5:sum([MATH] <NUM> 1:abs(L3 [−] L4 [)] [)] [÷] 15 [ENTER] for the last three lines in screen 9.

This is the *Mean of the Absolute Values of the Deviations*, or MAD = **102.358**.

7. With **Plot1** still set up as shown in screen 2, set up **Plot2**, as shown in screen 10.

Press [TRACE] for the plot of the original data with the exponentially smoothed values through it (see screen 11).

Second Try

To see if we can get a better fit, we will try other values of α. We want to follow the more current values a bit closer so we will increase α to α = **0.3**.

1. Press [2nd] [ENTRY] four times (or until your last line is like the first line in screen 5).

As in the first line of screen 12, change **0.2** to **0.3**, and then press [ENTER] for the **1** in the second line of screen 12.

2. Press [2nd] [ENTRY] a few times until you have the next three lines shown in screen 12. Press [ENTER] until you get an error message (this may take about 16 presses).

3. Select **1:Quit**, and then press [STAT] **1:Edit** and use the cursor control keys to go to the last value of **L4** for the forecast for the next period:

F_{17} = 841.67 or 842 customers.

4. Use [DEL] to delete the last value in **L4** so that **L3**, **L4**, and **L5** are all the same length (15 rows).

5. Use [2nd] [QUIT] to return to the home screen, and then press [2nd] [ENTRY] a few times until you recall the line necessary to calculate the MSE, as shown in screen 14.

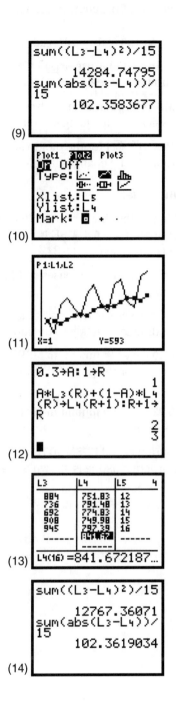

(9)

(10)

(11)

(12)

(13)

(14)

6. Press ENTER for MSE = 12767.

    With a similar use of 2nd [ENTRY], calculate MAD, as shown in screen 14 for MAD = 102.362.

    MSE has been reduced from 14284 to 12767, and MAD basically is unchanged from 102.358 to 102.362.

7. Press TRACE for the plot in screen 15 that responds more to the changes in sales.

Further Tries

Seeking further improvement, we proceed as in the Second Try, but with α = **0.4**. MSE is reduced further to 12494, but MAD is increased to 103.34.

With α = **0.5**, MSE increases to 12695, and MAD increases to 105.68.

The plot in screen 16 shows that the forecast might be responding too quickly to the most recent value of data.

α = **0.39** gave the minimum MSE = 12493 with a forecast of 863 customers for the period 17, or the first quarter of the fifth year.

α = **0.22** gave the minimum MAD = 101.80 with a forecast of 817 customers.

A program called **EXSMOOTH** automates the above procedure. This program listing is shown at right.

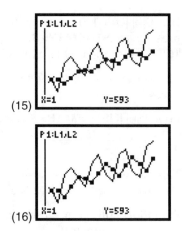

(15)

(16)

PROGRAM EXSMOOTH

```
FnOff :ClrHome
PlotsOff
PlotsOn 3
0→Yscl
Disp "TIME(1,2,3..N)"
Disp "IN L1, Y IN L2."
Pause :ClrHome
Menu("CONT OR
QUIT","CONTINUE",A,"QUIT",B)
Lbl B
ClrHome:Stop
Lbl A:dim(L1→N
ClrDraw
Plot3(xyLine,L1,L2,·)
ZoomStat:Trace
Xmax+1→Xmax
Input "ALPHA=",A:L2→L4
L2(1)→L4(2)
For(I,2,N-1)
L2(I)*A+(1-A)*L4(I)→L4(I+1)
End
A*L2(N)+(1-A)*L4(N)→P
PlotsOn 2
Plot2(xyLine,L1,L4,□)
DispGraph
Pt-On(N+1,P,2)
Trace
Output(3,1,"FORCAST AT T=")
Output(3,14,N+1)
Output(4,5,P)
L2-L4→L5
sum((L5²)/(N-1)→D
sum((abs(L5)/(N-1)→E
Output(6,1,"MSE="
Output(6,5,D)
Output(7,1,"MAD="
Output(7,5,E)
Pause :ClrHome
Return
```

Topic 55—Multiplicative Model (Program FORECAST)

For the multiplicative time-series model, we assume the **Y** data value is made up of three components: $Y = T * S * I$, where T, S, and I stand for the *trend, seasonal,* and *irregular* components. (See *Statistics for Business and Economics 6th Edition*, Anderson, Sweeney, and Williams, West Publishing Company.) Other textbooks include a C or a *"cyclical"* component. (See *Business Statistics* by Triola and Franklin, Addison Wesley Publishing Company.)

Because the calculations are tedious, we will be using program **FORECAST**. This program is available from Texas Instruments over the internet (www.ti.com) or on disk (1-800-TI-CARES) and can be transferred to your TI-83 with TI-GRAPH LINK. (The program listing is in Appendix B.)

We will use the data for customer count given at the beginning of this activity with the period stored in **L1** and the count in **L2**. We must use quarterly or monthly data for complete years for the program to work.

1. Press [PRGM] **<EXEC>**, highlight program **FORECAST**, and then press [ENTER] to paste the program name to the home screen, as shown in screen 17.

    Press [ENTER] again for the instructions shown in screen 18.

2. Press [ENTER] to continue.

    The data is automatically plotted with the period, or time, on the x-axis and the sales on the y-axis, as shown in screen 19.

    You are in Trace mode, so you can use the cursor control keys to go from point to point.

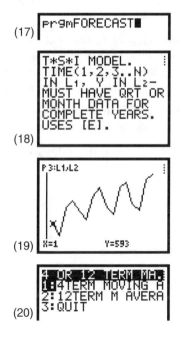

(17)

(18)

(19)

(20)

Activity 12, Forecasting (cont.)

3. Press ENTER, and you are given the options shown in screen 20.

   Because you have quarterly data, press **1:4 TERM MOVING A**(verage) for screen 21. (See Note.)

   We see from the plot in screen 21 that the four-term moving average is a very good smoother for the quarterly data. The graph is in Trace mode, so you can go from point to point on either curve.

4. Press ENTER for the next plot shown in screen 22.

   This last plot (screen 22) is the original data and the deseasonalized data plotted in Trace mode. Looking at the data, we decide to fit a linear least squares fit line to the deseasonalized data as our predictor of the trend.

5. Press ENTER for the menu of choices shown in screen 23.

6. Select **1:LinReg(a+bx)** for the plot shown in screen 24. (Notice the other choices available on the menu.) The original data, the deseasonalized data, and the linear trend line are all shown on this plot.

7. Press ENTER for the next plot shown in screen 25. The plot shows the original data, but this time with black squares so you can compare it with the forecast for the next year that is given as open squares.

8. Press ENTER for a list of the seasonal indexes given to three decimal places, as shown in screen 26.

   Use ▶ to read the index for the fourth quarter.

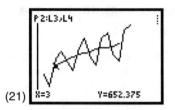

(21)

Note: *If you wish to fit a trend line to the moving average of the data (as in the Triola and Franklin reference) instead of to the deseasonalized data, make the following modifications to program FORECAST, and then skip to step 5.*

(I) Replace the following line of code
   `Plot2(xyLine,L1,L5,)Text(Ø, 36,"DESEASONALIZED"):Trace`
   with : `L3 → A1: L4 → A2.`

(ii) Replace L1, L5 with ʟA1,ʟA5 after `LinReg(a+bx)`, `QuadReg`, *and* `ExpReg` *in the fourth, sixth, and eighth lines after the line in (i).*

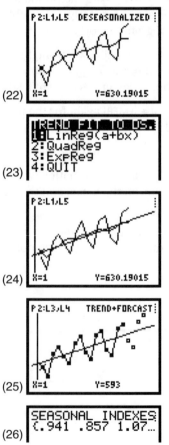

(22)

(23)

(24)

(25)

(26)

9. Press ENTER and you get the forecast values for the next year (screen 27).

10. Press ENTER again, and the MSE and MAD are given (screen 27) as discussed in Topic 54.

   These values are much smaller for this technique than they were for exponential smoothing because the periodic seasonal effect is more directly involved in this forecast.

11. Press ENTER for the instructive information shown in screen 28, which informs you how the calculated values are stored in matrix [E]. The last two lines remind you how to get back to the final graph. (We will investigate screen 28 more later in this topic.)

12. Do as suggested in the last two lines of screen 28 by pressing TRACE for screen 29.

13. Use ⊡ to get to the Trend line. Type **17**, and then press ENTER for the coordinates shown in screen 29. For the first quarter of the next year, period 17, the Trend value is **865.2**. Since the seasonal index is less than 1 (0.941),we forecast a value below the line of **865.2** ∗ **0.941 = 814.1532** or, if we carried all the decimals of the TI-83, we would have **814.14728**, as shown in screen 27.

   Notice at the top of screen 29, the **Y₁** $= a + b * x$ is turned on. As shown in screen 30, you can paste the a and b values using VARS **5:Statistics.<EQ> 2:a** and **3:b**. The slope is **14.58** or about 15.

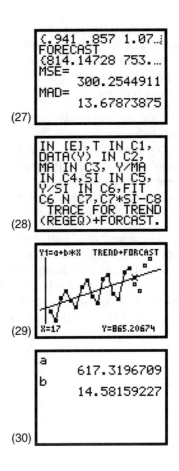

(27)

(28)

(29)

(30)

We revisit the last screen of program **FORECAST** (screen 31). The screen gives the contents of matrix [E], which was used for the previous plots and calculations.

MA in the third line of screen 31 stands for the *centered four-term moving averages* in column 3 of screen 32. Since moving averages cannot be calculated for the first two values, the table shows **1E-8** as a filler or missing value symbol. This is true in other columns as well.

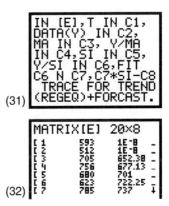

(31)

(32)

Screen 33 gives the first seven rows of columns 4- 8 of **Matrix [E]**. **SI** in column 5 stands for *seasonal index*. Notice how values in column 5 repeat every four quarters and are calculated from the means of the same quarter data in column 4 (adjusted so all the seasonal indices add to four).

```
MATRIX[E]  20×8     [E]  20×8
_ [E-8     .94099   630.19 _  631.9    [E-8    ]
_ 1E-8     .8565    597.78 _  646.48   1E-8    ]
_ 1.0807   1.0788   653.52 _  661.06   1E-8    ]
_ 1.1165   1.1237   672.76 _  675.65   1E-8    ]
_ .97004   .94099   722.65 _  690.23   1E-8    ]
_ .86258   .8565    727.38 _  704.81   1E-8    ]
_ 1.0651   1.0788   727.68 ↓  719.39   1E-8    ↓
```

(33)

Y÷SI is the deseasonalized data in column 6. A least squares linear regression line was fitted to column 6 data. The resulting equation ($Y = a + bX$) had the periods, or Xs, in column 1 substituted in this equation for the values in column 7. Notice each value in column 7 increases by approximately 15 from the previous value. Fifteen is the slope of the line, as we discovered in step 13 above.

```
MATRIX[E]  20×8     X[E]  20×8
_ .85156   .8565    807.94 ↑  821.46   1E-8    ↑
_ 1E-8     1.0788   841.69 _  836.04   1E-8    ]
_ 1E-8     1.1237   840.95 _  850.63   1E-8    ]
_ 1E-8     .94099   1E-8   _  865.21   [E-8    ]
_ 1E-8     .8565    1E-8   _  879.79   753.54  ]
_ 1E-8     1.0788   1E-8   _  894.37   964.83  ]
_ 1E-8     1.1237   [E-8   _  908.95   1021.4  ]
20,6=1E-8                    814.147282...
```

(34)

Screen 34 gives rows 14-20 of columns 4-8 of **Matrix [E]**. Notice the period 17 (first quarter of the fifth year) value of the trend forecast in column 7 is **865.21**, as also shown in step 13. If the trend value is multiplied by the seasonal index value in column 5, or **0.94099**, we obtain **865.21 ∗ 0.94099 = 814.15**, as in the forecast in column 8.

EXPLORATIONS

Activity 13

Some Nonparametric Tests

There are many nonparametric methods. Many of these use the ranks of the sample data obtained by sorting the data. We will cover four topics to give an idea of what is possible with the TI-83. Topics 56 and 57 on the Sign Test and the Wilcoxon Signed-Ranks Test are the nonparametric counterparts to the two-sample t test for dependent data in Topic 44. Topics 58 and 59 on the Mann-Whitney-Wilcoxon Test and the Randomization Test (re-sampling) are the nonparametric counterparts to the two-sample t test for independent samples in Topic 44.

Topic 56—Sign Test for Two Dependent Samples

To test the claim that a blood pressure medication reduces the diastolic blood pressure, a random sample of ten people with high blood pressure had their pressures recorded. After a few weeks on the medication, their pressures were recorded again. See the data in the table below.

Subject	1	2	3	4	5	6	7	8	9	10
Before (L_1):	94	87	105	92	102	85	110	95	92	93
After (L_2):	87	88	93	87	92	88	96	87	92	86
L_1 - L_2 = L_3	+	−	+	+	+	−	+	+	0	+

Activity 13, Some Nonparametric Tests (cont.)

Letting p represent the proportion in the population whose blood pressure would be reduced by the medication (+ in the above samples), we want to test the following hypotheses:

$H_0 : p = 0.5 \quad H_a: p > 0.5$

If the medication has no effect on the blood pressure reading, we would expect about half to do better after taking the medication and half to do worse. The zero difference does not add any information; therefore, we see that of the nine subjects, there are two negative signs and seven positive signs. We would expect 4.5 of each (the average in the long run). This is a binomial distribution with $N = 9$ and $P = 0.5$.

P-value and Conclusion

We will use [2nd] [DISTR] **A:binomcdf(9** ⬜ **0.5** ⬜ **2** ⬜ [ENTER] for screen 1, or a p-value of **0.0898**, which is the probability of getting two or less negative signs. We could also have found the probability of getting seven or more positives, also shown in screen 1.

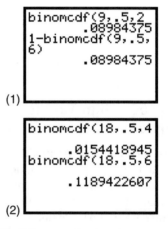

(1)

We have very little evidence to reject the null hypothesis that the medication has no effect. (Not significant at the $\alpha = 0.05$ level.)

If the sample size were doubled to 18 and the number of negatives doubled to 4, we would reach the opposite conclusion. (See screen 2.) With the larger sample size, however, we could also see a larger proportion of negatives (for example, six or more), and again, we would not be able to reject the null hypothesis.

(2)

Note: If the sample sizes become greater than 999, you could use the normal distribution to approximate the binomial (as in Topic 24) because it would only take samples greater than size 20 to meet the criteria needed for this approximation with **p** = 0.5 ($n * p$ and $n * (1 - p) \geq 10$).

If there is sufficient data, the Sign Test is easy to use and explain. When we used more than the sign of the difference of the blood pressure readings for the more restrictive t test in Topic 44, "Dependent Samples," we had strong evidence (p-value = 0.0047) that the medication reduced the pressure. Not rejecting the null hypothesis does not mean that the null hypothesis is true; we just have insufficient evidence to say it is false.

The next topic is less restrictive than the t test but uses more of the information available in the sample than does the sign test.

Topic 57—Wilcoxon Signed-Ranks Test for Two Dependent Samples

To test the claim that a blood pressure medication reduces the diastolic blood pressure, a random sample of ten people with high blood pressure had their pressures recorded. After a few weeks on the medication their pressure was recorded again. See the data in the table below.

Subject	1	2	3	4	5	6	7	8	9	10
Before (L_1):	94	87	105	92	102	85	110	95	92	93
After (L_2):	87	88	93	87	92	88	96	87	92	86
$L_1 - L_2 = L_3$	7	-1	12	5	10	-3	14	8	0	7

Use the following procedure to test the following hypotheses:

H_0 : The populations of blood pressures are identical.
H_a: The population on medication is shifted to the left.

1. Put the Before readings in L_1 and the After readings in L_2.

2. Highlight L_3, and then enter L_1 ⊟ L_2 for the bottom line, as shown in screen 3. Press [ENTER] to complete the calculation, as shown in screen 4.

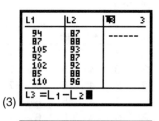
(3)

3. Highlight L_4, and then press [MATH] <NUM> 1:abs(L_3 for the bottom line, as shown in screen 4. Press [ENTER], and all the values in L_4 will be positive.

4. Press [STAT] 2:SortA(L_4 ⌑ L_3 [ENTER].

   The values in L_4 will be sorted with the smallest value zero coming first. List L_3 will take along the corresponding values (0 comes first even though -3 is the smallest number in L_3). See the results in screen 5.

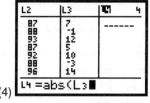
(4)

5. Put the ranks of the data in L_4 into L_5 as follows.

   a. Rank **0** as 0.

   b. Rank **1** and **3** as -1 and -2 (negative because they are from negative differences in L_3).

   c. Rank **5** as 3.

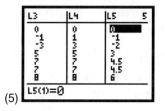
(5)

   d. Rank the two **7s** by averaging the fourth and fifth ranks (or $(4 + 5)/2 = $ **4.5**).

   e. Rank the other values, which are all different and positive, as 6, 7, 8, and 9.

Activity 13, Some Nonparametric Tests (cont.)

The sum of the integers from 1 to $n = (1 + n) * n/2$; thus, the sum of the integers from 1 to $9 = (1 + 9) * 9/2 = $ **45**. $T = $ **sum(L5** = **39** is our test statistic. (See screen 6)

As a check on your work, note that half the difference between the above two values is the absolute value of the sum of the negative ranks, or $abs (-1 + -2) = 3$.

(6)

What is the probability of getting a sum of 39 by chance if there are no differences in the two populations?

All possible ranks from 1 to 9, positive or negative, are possible. This is $2^9 = 512$ possibilities.

P-Value and Conclusion

The five ways of getting a sum of 39 or more are listed in the table below. Thus, the p-value $= 5/512 = 0.009765 = $ **0.01**.

There is strong evidence that the medication has decreased the blood pressure.

±1	±2	±3	±4	±5	±6	±7	±8	±9	sum
-1	-2	3	4	5	6	7	8	9	39
1	2	-3	4	5	6	7	8	9	39
1	-2	3	4	5	6	7	8	9	41
-1	2	3	4	5	6	7	8	9	43
1	2	3	4	5	6	7	8	9	45

Charts in Text and Normal Approximation

As a sample size increases, it can be a bit tedious to calculate all of the possibilities. Texts will have a chart for small sample sizes (some texts base their chart on the smallest sum of the positives or negatives, -3 in our example). For sizes larger than the charts can handle, the normal approximation below gives good results.

Mean: $\mu_T = 0$ Standard Deviation: $\sigma_T = \sqrt{(n(n + 1)(2n + 1)/6)}$.

If the two populations are the same, we would expect an equal number of positive and negative ranks of their differences. Thus, on average, the sum of the ranks should be zero.

(7)

$z = (T \pm 0.5 - \mu_T)/\sigma_T = (39 - 0.5 - 0)/\sqrt{(9 * 10 * 19/6)} = $ **2.28**, where the -0.5 is a continuity correction. For the right tail, we start at 38.5 to include the class of 39. The area in the right tail of the normal distribution is a p-value of $0.0113 = $ **0.01** (see Topic 24), very close to the exact value above. (See screen 7.)

Topic 58– Wilcoxon (Mann-Whitney) Test for Two Independent Samples

Test the claim that teaching Method A results in higher test scores than Method B based on the following scores from random samples of students taught with the two methods.

							mean	Sx	n
Method A (L1)	40	38	39	32	35	38	37	2.966	6
Method B (L2)	34	36	31	37	29		33.4	3.362	5

We will test the following hypotheses:

H_0 : The two population distributions are identical.

H_a: Population A is to the right of population B.

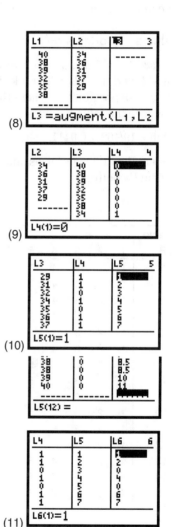

1. Put the Method A scores in **L1** and the Method B scores in **L2**.

2. Highlight **L3**, and then press ENTER **[LIST]** <OPS> **9:augment(L1** ⬚ **L2** for the bottom line, as shown in screen 8. Press ENTER and **L1** is pasted above **L2** in **L3**, as shown in screen 9.

3. Put zeros next to the six values of the largest sample, Method A, in **L4** and ones next to the five values of Method B. (See screen 9.)

4. Use STAT **2:SortA(L3** ⬚ **L4** ENTER to sort the data in **L3** and carry the method identification (0 or 1) in **L4**, as shown in screen 10.

5. Put the ranks of the values in **L3** in **L5** from 1 for the lowest score of 29, to 11 for the highest score of 40 (screen 10). Because there are two 38s, they both get the mean of the eighth and ninth rank, or 8.5.

6. Highlight **L6**, and then press **L4** ✕ **L5** ENTER for the ranks of Method B in **L6** (screen 11). Zeros are in the rows where the ranks of Method A are in L5.

    To check your work, the sum of n ranks is $(1 + n)n/2 = (1 + 11)11/2 =$ **66**, which should be the sum of **L5**.

Press 2nd [LIST] <MATH> 5:sum(L5 ENTER for **66**, as shown in screen 12. The test statistic $T = $ **sum(** L6 $= 20$ is the sum of the ranks for the smaller sample.

The average rank value is (the sum of ranks)/$n = 66/11 = 6$. The smaller sample of five values has an average rank of $20/5 = 4$ and a total of 20 instead of the expected $5 * 6 = 30$. Is this difference significantly less than what we would expect if the data came from identical populations?

```
(1+11)11/2
                    66
sum(L5
                    66
sum(L6
                    20
```
(12)

P-value and Conclusion

There are 462 (11 nCr 5 = 462) ways of picking five ranks for Method B and the other six ranks for Method A (see Topic 22). There are 19 possibilities where the sum of the five ranks is 20 or less (see the table below).

P-value $= 19/462 = 0.0411$.

We reject the null hypothesis and conclude that Method A does significantly better.

sample B	rank											sum
	1	2	3	4	5	6	7	8	9	10	11	
1	1	2	3	4	5							15
2	1	2	3	4		6						16
3	1	2	3	4			7					17
4	1	2	3	4				8				18
5	1	2	3	4					9			19
6	1	2	3	4						10		20
7	1	2	3		5	6						17
8	1	2	3		5		7					18
9	1	2	3					8				19
10	1	2	3						9			20
11	1	2	3			6	7					19
12	1	2	3			6		8				20
13	1	2		4	5	6						18
14	1	2		4	5		7					19
15	1	2		4	5			8				20
16	1	2		4		6	7					20
17	1		3	4	5	6						19
18	1		3	4	5		7					20
19		2	3	4	5	6						20

Charts in Texts and Normal Approximation

It is tedious to calculate all the values in the previous table, and it is not necessary because texts covering this topic have charts for your use. If your sample sizes are too large for the table, you can use the following normal approximation.

Let n be the smaller sample size and m the larger.

Mean for smaller sample:
$$\mu_T = n(n + m + 1)/2 = 5(5 + 6 + 1)/2 = 30$$

Standard deviation:
$$\sigma_T = \sqrt{(n * m * (n + m + 1)/12)} = \sqrt{(5 * 6 * 12/12)} = 5.477$$

$$z = (T \pm 0.5 - \mu_T)/\sigma_T = (20 + 0.5 - 30)/5.477 = -1.734$$

The 0.5 is the continuity correction as we want the area to the left, including the class with 20 that ends at 20.5.

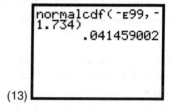

Find the area in the left tail of the normal distribution, or an approximate p-value = **0.0415** (very close to the exact value of 0.0411 in the previous section), by pressing 2nd [DISTR] **2:normalcdf(** (-) **E99** , (-) **1.734** ENTER. (See screen 13.)

(13)

Notice that these p-values are less than 0.0493, the value obtained with the more restrictive t test in "Testing Independent Samples" in Topic 44.

Topic 59—Randomization Test for Two Independent Samples

Test the claim that teaching Method A results in higher test scores than Method B based on the following scores from random samples of students taught with the two methods.

							mean	Sx	n
Method A (L1)	40	38	39	32	35	38	37	2.966	6
Method B (L2)	34	36	31	37	29		33.4	3.362	5

Use the following procedure to test the following hypotheses:

$H_0 : \mu_A - \mu_B = 0$ from identical populations

$H_a: \mu_A - \mu_B > 0$

Activity 13, Some Nonparametric Tests (cont.)

1. Put the Method A scores in **L₁** and the B scores in **L₂**.

   You will need program **RAN2IND**. This listing is given at the end of this topic.

2. Set the random seed as explained in Topic 21 and in the first two lines in screen 14.

3. Press [PRGM], and then highlight program **RAND2IND** so **prgmRAN2IND** is pasted to the home screen.

4. Press [ENTER] for screen 15 that reminds you to put the two samples in **L₁** and **L₂**. Press [ENTER] again, and you get the menu screen. (See screen 16.)

5. Select **1:N=100** for the next screen 17, which tells you the difference between the means of the two samples is **3.6**. Press [ENTER] and the program takes the mean of five randomly selected values from the combined pool of 11 values.

   The 11 values are a representative sample taken from the null hypothesis identical populations. The program will subtract the mean of the five selected values from the mean of the remaining six values and compare it to 3.6. If the difference of the two means is 3.6 or greater, this fact is recorded.The difference of means is stored in **L₆**.

   This process is repeated 100 times. You see from the results of the 100 repetitions in screen 18 that getting a difference of 3.6 happened four times out of 100 for an estimated p-value of **0.04** (0.08 for a two-tail test). (If you used another seed or a different number of repetitions, your answer could differ.)

6. Press [ENTER], and the **Histogram** of all the differences is shown, as shown in screen 19. Use[TRACE] to see that values of 3.6 or greater are in the right tail. If values of 3.6 or greater were a more common occurrence, the values would be more toward the center of the distribution, and you would fail to reject the null hypothesis.

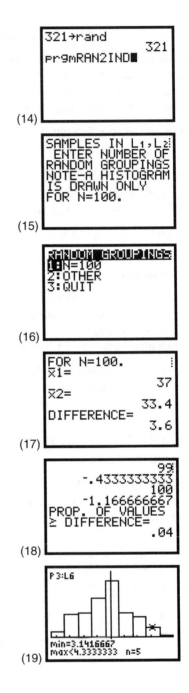

(14)

(15)

(16)

(17)

(18)

(19)

Note that this test is very much like Topic 58, but in Topic 58, you were concerned with all possible totals (or equivalently means) of size 5. Here, you do the same thing, but rather than theoretically figure out the number of possibilities, you just randomly generate them with the actual sample data rather than their ranks. No need to worry about ties.

If you look at the stat list editor or the spreadsheet, you see that the values of the differences have been taken out of their original order in **L6** and placed in descending order in **L4**. (See screens 20 and 21 for the first 12 values.)

The four largest values were **4.3333**, **3.9667**, **3.9667** and **3.6**.

L5 has the last randomly assigned samples. The first five values represent the smaller sample, or Method B {32, 37, 39, 34, 38}. The remaining six values represent Method A {29, 36, 35, 40, 31, 38}. (See screens 20 and 21.)

If you go down to the bottom of **L6**, or look at screen 18 again, or use **L6** ⬚ **100** ⬚, as shown in screen 22, you will see the difference of the last means is **-1.167**.

The program can be rerun with different values of N, but a **Histogram** will not be automatically plotted.

The program listing is on the next page.

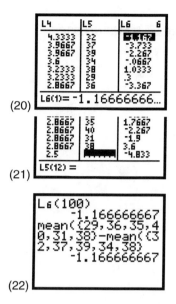

(20)

(21)

(22)

Note: It is a coincidence that -1.1667 was also the mean of the first sample.

Program RAN2IND.83P

```
ClrDraw:ClrHome:ClrList L5,L6
0→P
Disp "SAMPLES IN L1,L2"
Disp " ENTER NUMBER OF"
Disp "RANDOM GROUPINGS"
Disp "NOTE-A HISTOGRAM"
Disp "IS DRAWN ONLY"
Disp "FOR N=100.":Pause
Menu("RANDOM
GROUPINGS","N=100",A,"OTHER",B,"QUIT",
C)
Lbl C:Stop
Lbl A
100→K:Goto D
Lbl B:Disp "N=":Input K
Lbl D
1-Var Stats L1
x̄→A:Σx→E:n→M
1-Var Stats L2
x̄→B:Σx→F:n→N
abs((A-B)→D
E+F→T:M+N→L
Disp "x̄1=",A
Disp "x̄2=",B
Disp "DIFFERENCE=",D
Pause
L1→L5:M+1→J:For(I,1,N):L2(I)→L5(J):1+J
→J:End
For(I,1,K)
L→C:1→J:0→S
If A>B:Then:M→Z:Else:N→Z:End
For(J,1,Z)
int((C*rand+1)→V:S+L5(V)→S
L5(C)→H
L5(V)→L5(C)
H→L5(V)
C-1→C:End
If A>B:Then:S/M-(T-S)/N→U:Else:S/N-(T-
S)/M→U:End
If K<101:U→L6(I)
If U≥D:1+P→P
Disp I,U
End
Disp "PROP. OF VALUES"
Disp "≥ DIFFERENCE="
Disp P/K:Pause
If K≠100:Stop
L6→L4
SortD(L4)
FnOff :PlotsOff :PlotsOn
3:Plot3(Histogram,L6,1):ZoomStat
Return
```

APPENDIX A

Cross-References to Two Statistics Textbooks

This appendix cross-references topics in this handbook to *The Basic Practice of Statistics* and to *Elementary Statistics 6th Edition*.

The table at the right relates text sections from *The Basic Practice of Statistics* (David S. Moore, Freeman Publishing Company) to topics in the *Statistics Handbook for the TI-83*.

Moore text	TI-83 topic	subject
1.1	1, 2	Histograms
	3, 9	Stem-and-leaf plots, Time plots
1.2	4, 6	Measures of center, Measures of spread, Boxplots
1.3	24	Normal distribution
2.1	7	Scatter plots
2.2	8	Correlation
2.3	11, 15	Least-squares regression, Influential observations
2.5	18, 17	Categorical data and two-way tables, Bar charts
3.1, 2	19	Designing samples and experiments (random numbers)
4.1	25, 21	Sample proportions, Coin toss
4.2	23	Probability histogram of discrete distribution (example: binomial)
4.3	25	Normal approximation for sample proportions
4.4	23	Binomial distributions
4.5	26	Distribution of sample means and the Central Limit Theorem
4.6	10	Control charts
5.1	33	Confidence interval and test for mean (σ known) and sample size
5.2	40	Test of significance for mean (σ known)
6.1	34, 41	Confidence interval and test for mean (σ unknown)
	37, 44	Matched pairs t procedure
6.2	37, 44	Comparing two means C.I. and t test
6.3	46	F test for two standard deviations
7.1	35, 42	One population proportion C.I. and z test and sample size
7.2	38, 45	Comparing two proportions C.I. and z test
8.1	48	Inference for two-way tables
9.1	49	One-way analysis of variance
10.1	52, 53	Inference for regression

The table at the right relates text sections from *Elementary Statistics 6th Edition* (Mario F. Triola, Addison-Wesley Publishing Company) to topics in the *Statistics Handbook for the TI-83*.

Triola text	TI-83 topic	subject
1-4	19	Methods of sampling (random sampling)
2-2, 3	1, 2	Frequency and relative frequency tables and histograms
2-4, 5	4	Measures of central tendency, Measures of variation
2-6	5	Measures of position
2-7	3, 6	Stem-and leaf plots, Box plots
3-1	21	Law of large numbers (coin toss)
3-5	29, 30	Probabilities through simulations
3-6	22	Factorials, permutations, and Combinations
4-2	23	Probability histogram with mean and standard deviation
4-3	23, 31	Binomial distribution, Poisson distribution
4-4	23	Mean and standard deviation of a binomial distribution
5-2, 3	24	Normal distributions
5-4	26	Central Limit Theorem
5-5	24	Normal approximation to the binomial distribution (last part)
6-2	33, 34	Estimating a population mean: σ known and σ unknown
6-3	35	Estimating a population proportion
6-4	36	Estimating a population standard deviation
7-3	40	Testing a claim about a mean: large sample
7-4	41	Testing a claim about a mean: small sample (σ unknown)
7-5	42	Testing a claim about a proportion
7-6	43	Testing a claim about a standard deviation
8-2	44, 37	Inference about two means: dependent samples (test, C.I.)
8-3	44, 37, 28	Inference about two means: independent large samples, Variance of difference of two means
8-4	46	Comparing two variances (standard deviations)
8-5	44, 37	Inference about two means: independent small samples
8-6	45, 38	Inference about two proportions (hypothesis test, C.I.)
9-2 to 4	52	Correlation, regression, prediction intervals
9-5	53	Multiple regression
10-2	47	Multinomial experiments
10-3	48	Contingency tables
11-2, 3	49	One-way ANOVA
11-4	50, 51	Two-way ANOVA
12	10	Control charts
13-2 to 4	56 to 58	Sign Test, Wilcoxon Signed-Ranks and Rank-Sum Tests

Program Listings for A1ANOVA, A2MULREG, and FORECAST

You can access these programs from your instructor, or over the internet at www.ti.com, or by calling Texas Instruments at 1-800-TI-CARES.

Program A1ANOVA.83p

```
Menu("ANOVA USES[D][E]","ONE-WAY
ANOVA",P,"RAN BLOCK DESIGN",Q,"2WAY
FACTORIAL",R,"QUIT",S)
Lbl S:Stop
Lbl P
Disp "1. USE A N*2 MAT":Disp
"[D],OBSERVATIONS":Disp "IN COL 1,
FACTOR":Disp "LEVEL IN COL 2-":Disp "INTEGERS
1,2..N."
Disp "2. ENTER MEAN,SD":Disp "AND SAMP
SIZES."
Pause :ClrHome
Lbl 5:ClrHome
Menu("DATA INPUT WITH","DATA MAT
[D]",2,"x̄1,Sx1,n1,x̄2..",1,"QUIT",3)
Lbl 3:ClrHome
Stop
Lbl 1:ClrHome
9→F:Disp "HOW MANY LEVELS"
Input N
N→dim(L₄:N→dim(L₅:N→dim(L₆:0→G
0→T
For(I,1,N)
Disp "LEVEL",I:Input "MEAN=?",V:V→L₄(I)
Input "S.D.=?",V:V→L₅(I)
Input "SIZE=?",V:V→L₆(I)
L₆(I)+G→G
L₄(I)*L₆(I)+T→T:End
T/G→M:0→R:0→S
For(I,1,N)
S+(M-L₄(I))² L₆(I)→S:R+(L₅(I))²*(L₆(I)-
1)→R:End
S/(N-1)→D
R/(G-N)→E
Goto 4
Lbl 2:ClrHome
1→F:dim([D]:Ans(1)→G:2→N
For(I,1,G)
If [D](I,2)>N
[D](I,2)→N:End
N→dim(L₄:N→dim(L₅:N→dim(L₆:Fill(0,L₄):Fill(0,
L₅):Fill(0,L₆):0→T:0→S:{N,4}→dim([E]
For(I,1,G)
T+[D](I,1)→T
S+([D](I,1))²→S:[D](I,2)→B
L₅(B)+1→L₅(B)
L₄(B)+[D](I,1)→L₄(B):L₆(B)+([D](I,1))²→L₆(B):
End
S-T²/G→P:0→A
For(I,1,N)
A+(L₄(I))²/L₅(I)→A:End
A-T²/G→S:P-S→R
S/(N-1)→D
R/(G-N)→E
Lbl 4
ClrHome
Disp "   DF   SS"
```

```
Output(2,1,"FAC":Output(2,5,N-
1):Output(2,8,S)
Output(3,1,"ERR":Output(3,5,(G-
N)):Output(3,8,R)
Output(5,3,"F=":Output(5,5,round((D/E),2))
Output(6,3,"P=":Fix 3
Output(6,5,round(Fcdf(D/E,ε99,N-1,G-
N),3):Float
Output(7,2,"SP=":Output(7,5,√(E):Pause
ClrHome
If F=9:Goto V
Disp "[LEV N MEAN SD]"
For(I,1,N)
I→[E](I,1)
L₅(I)→[E](I,2)
L₄(I)/L₅(I)→M
M→[E](I,3)
(L₆(I)-(L₄(I))²/L₅(I))/(L₅(I)-1)→V
√(V→[E](I,4)
End:Pause [E]
Lbl V:ClrHome
G-N→C
1.96(1+2/(1+8*C))→W
C*(e^(W*W/C)-1)→C:√(C)→C
C*√(E→W
ClrList L₂,L₃
If 9=F:Then
For(I,1,N,1)
W/√((L₆(I))→Z
L₄(I)-Z→L₂(I)
L₄(I)+Z→L₃(I)
End:Else
For(I,1,N,1)
W/√((L₅(I))→Z
L₄(I)/L₅(I)-Z→L₂(I)
L₄(I)/L₅(I)+Z→L₃(I):End:End
(max(L₃)-min(L₂))/10→W
min(L₂)-W→Xmin
max(L₃)+W→Xmax
0→Xscl:0→Yscl
1→Ymin:192→Ymax:120/(N+1)→H
PlotsOff :FnOff :ClrDraw
Text(1,1,"0.95 CI.S -LEVEL 1 AT TOP")
H+40→Y
For(I,N,1,-1)
Line(L₂(I),Y,L₃(I),Y)
Y+H→Y:End
Trace:Pause
ClrHome:Stop
Lbl Q:ClrHome
Disp "DATA IN N*3 MAT":Disp
"[D].OBSERVATIONS"
Disp "COL 1,COL 2(A)+":Disp "COL 3(B)
CONTAIN"
Disp "FACTOR LEVEL AND":Disp "BLOCK-INTEGERS"
Disp "1,2..."
Goto 9
Lbl R:ClrHome
```

```
Disp "EQUAL REPLICATES":Disp "DATA IN N*3 MAT
":Disp "[D],1ST COL-DATA":Disp "2ND COL-A
LEVELS":Disp "3RD COL-B LEVELS":Disp "LEVELS-
INTEGERS":Disp "STARTING WITH 1."
Lbl 9
Pause :ClrHome
Menu("CONT OR QUIT","CONTINUE",A,"QUIT",B)
Lbl B:ClrHome:Stop
Lbl A
dim([D]):Ans(1)→R:2→K:1→L
For(I,1,R)
If [D](I,3)>K
[D](I,3)→K
If [D](I,2)>L
[D](I,2)→L:End
K→dim(L₆:K→dim(L₅:Fill(0,L₆):Fill(0,L₅):L→dim
(L₄:L→dim(L₃:Fill(0,L₄):Fill(0,L₃):0→T:0→S
For(I,1,R)
T+[D](I,1)→T
S+([D](I,1))²→S:[D](I,3)→C
[D](I,2)→D
L₅(C)+1→L₅(C)
L₃(D)+1→L₃(D)
L₆(C)+[D](I,1)→L₆(C):L₄(D)+[D](I,1)→L₄(D):End
S-T²/R→G:0→A
For(I,1,K)
A+(L₆(I))²/L₅(I)→A:End
0→B:For(I,1,L)
B+(L₄(I))²/L₃(I)→B:End
A-T²/R→U
B-T²/R→V
K*L→M:M→dim(L₃
Fill(0,L₃):1→I
For(J,1,K)
For(E,1,L)
For(F,1,R)
If (([D](F,3)=J)*([D](F,2)=E))
L₃(I)+[D](F,1)→L₃(I):End
1+I→I
End:End
0→Q
For(I,1,M)
Q+(L₃(I))²→Q
End
Q/(R/M)-U-V-T²/R→P:G-U-V-P→E
ClrHome
Disp "    DF    SS"
Output(2,1,"A":Output(2,4,L-1):Output(2,7,V)
Output(3,1,"B":Output(3,4,K-1):Output(3,7,U)
If (R/M)=1:Then:P→E:Output(4,1,"ER"):(K-
1)*(L-1)→Z:Goto E:End
Output(4,1,"AB")
Lbl E
Output(4,4,(K-1)*(L-
1)):Output(4,7,P):Output(5,1,"   ")
If (R/M)=1
Goto C

Output(5,1,"ER":Output(5,4,(R-
K*L)):Output(5,7,E):(R-K*L)→Z
Lbl C
Output(6,4,"F(A)=")
V/(L-1)/(E/Z)→F:Output(6,9,round(F,2)
Output(7,7,"P=":Fix 3
Output(7,9,round(Fcdf(F,ε99,L-1,Z),3):Float
Output(8,4,"F(B)=")
(U/(K-1))/(E/Z)→F:Output(8,9,round(F,2):Pause
:ClrHome
Output(1,1,"B      P=":Fix 3
Output(1,9,round(Fcdf(F,ε99,K-1,Z),3):Float
If (R/M)=1
Goto D
Output(2,3,"F(AB)=")
P/((K-1)*(L-1))/(E/(R-K*L))→F
Output(2,9,round(F,2))
Output(3,7,"P=":Fix 3
Output(3,9,round(Fcdf(F,ε99,L-1,R-
K*L),3):Float
Lbl D
√((E/Z)→S
Output(5,3,"S=":Output(5,5,S)
Return
```

Program A2MULREG.83p

```
ClrHome
Disp "DATA IN MAT [D]":Disp "COL
Y,X1,X2,..XN":Disp "Y MUST BE IN THE":Disp
"1ST COL OF [D]."
Disp "    "
Disp "[A],[B],[C],[D],"
Disp "[E]+[F] USED."
Pause :ClrHome
dim([D])→L₆:L₆(1)→N:L₆(2)→M
Menu("MULT REG+CORR","MULT
REGRESSION",1,"CORR MATRIX",X,"QUIT",Y)
Lbl 1
0→Z:0→dim(LYVAL:0→dim(LYHAT:0→dim(LRES:0→dim(
LSRES:0→dim(LLEVER:0→dim(LCOOKD
ClrHome:FnOff
Disp "HOW MANY IND VAR":Input
D:D+1→P:P→dim(L₅
M→L₅(P)
{N,P}→dim([E]
Fill(1,[E])
For(J,1,D)
Disp "COL. OF VAR.",J
Input H:H→L₅(J):End
If D≠1:Goto 3
Menu("SCATTER PLOT","YES PLOT",2,"NO",3)
Lbl 2
ClrList L₁,L₂
0→Xscl:0→Yscl
For(I,1,N)
[D](I,H)→L₁(I)
[D](I,1)→L₂(I)
End:PlotsOff
FnOn 6
LinReg(a+bx) L₁,L₂:"a+bX"→Y₆
PlotsOn 3:ExprOff:Plot3(Scatter,L₁,L₂,□)
ZoomStat:Trace
ExprOn
Lbl 3
For(J,1,D)
L₅(J)→C:J+1→K
For(I,1,N)
[D](I,C)→[E](I,K):End:End
{P,P}→dim([C]
([E]ᵀ*[E])⁻¹→[C]:{N,1}→dim([B]:0→Y:For(I,1,N)
[D](I,1)→[B](I,1):Y+[B](I,1)→Y
End
{P,1}→dim([A]
[C]*([E]ᵀ*[B])→[A]:0→A
For(I,1,N)
A+([B](I,1))²→A:End:0→B
[E]ᵀ*[B]→[F]
For(I,1,P)
B+[A](I,1)*[F](I,1)→B:End
A-B→E:N-P→F
√((E/F))→S:0→A
For(I,1,N)
A+([B](I,1))²→A:End:A-Y²/N→T
```

```
T-E→R:R/T→Q
(R/D)/(E/F)→V
1-(E/F)/(T/(N-1))→J
ClrHome
Output(1,1,"  DF SS")
Output(2,1,"RG"):Output(2,4,D):Output(2,7,R)
Output(3,1,"ER"):Output(3,4,F):Output(3,7,E):
Output(4,1,"  F="):Output(4,7,round(V,2))
Output(5,5,"P=":Fix
3:Output(5,7,round(Fcdf(V,ε99,D,F),3):Float:0
utput(6,2,"R-SQ="):Output(6,7,round(Q,4))
Output(7,2,"(ADJ)"):Output(7,7,round(J,4))
Output(8,1,"S="):Output(8,3,S)
Pause :ClrHome
Output(1,1,"B0="):[A](1,1)→H:Output(1,4,H)
1→A:0→B:D→C:0→E:Lbl 4:1→J
If C>3:Then:1→E:3+B→B:Else:B+C→B:End
Output(2,1,"CL COEFF / T  P")
For(I,A,B):I+1→K:Output(J+2,1,L₅(I))
[A](K,1)→H:Output(J+2,3,H)
[A](K,1)/(S*√([C](K,K)))→H:Output(J+3,5,round(
H,2):Fix 3
Output(J+3,12,round(2*tcdf(abs(H),ε99,F),3)
Float:2+J→J
End
If E=0:Goto 5
Pause :ClrHome
3+A→A:C-3→C:0→E:Goto 4
Lbl 5:Pause
Lbl A
Menu("MAIN MENU","CONF+PRI
INTERV",C,"RESIDUALS",R,"NEW
MODEL",1,"QUIT",Z)
Lbl C:ClrHome
Disp "FOR C.I. OR P.I.":Disp " D.F.
ERR.=",F:Input "T*=?",T
D→dim(L₆
{P,1}→dim([F]
Fill(1,[F])
Lbl D:ClrHome
For(I,1,D)
Disp "X FOR COL",L₅(I):Input V
I+1→K:V→L₆(I)
V→[F](K,1):End
[F]ᵀ*[A]
Ans(1,1)→H
[F]ᵀ*[C]*[F]
Ans(1,1)→Q
T*S*√(Q→E
ClrHome
Disp "C.I. FROM/TO",(H-E):Disp (H+E)
T*S*√((1+Q)→E
Disp "P.I. FROM/TO",(H-E):Disp
(H+E):Output(7,1,"YHAT="):Output(7,6,H):Pause
Menu("AGAIN OR RETURN","AGAIN",D,"MAIN
MENU",A,"QUIT",Z)
Lbl R
```

```
1→Z
PlotsOff :PlotsOn 3:ClrHome
FnOff :AxesOn
0→Xscl:0→Yscl
For(I,1,N)
[E]*[A]→[F]
[F](I,1)→ʟYHAT(I):[D](I,1)→ʟYVAL(I):ʟYVAL(I)-
ʟYHAT(I)→ʟRES(I)
End
{P,1}→dim([F]
For(I,1,N)
For(J,1,P)
[E](I,J)→[F](J,1):End
[C]*[F]→[B]
[F]ᵀ[B]
Ans(1,1)→ʟLEVER(I):End
For(I,1,N)
ʟRES(I)/(S*√((1-
ʟLEVER(I)))→ʟSRES(I):ʟRES(I)²*ʟLEVER(I)/(P*S²*
(1-ʟLEVER(I))²)→ʟCOOKD(I):End
SetUpEditor
ʟYVAL,ʟYHAT,ʟRES,ʟSRES,ʟLEVER,ʟCOOKD
Lbl U:ʟSRES→L₄
Menu("RES OR STAND RES","RESIDUAL
PLOT",S,"STAND.RES.PLOT",T,"DURBIN WATSON
D",W,"MAIN MENU",A,"QUIT",Z)
Lbl S:ClrHome
ʟRES→L₄:Goto V
Lbl T:ClrHome
Lbl V
Menu("PLOT OF RESID ","VS YHAT.",6,"VS AN IND
VAR.",7,"VS ROW NUMBER.",8,"PREVIOUS
MENU",U,"MAIN MENU",A,"QUIT",Z)
Lbl 7:ClrHome
Input "WHAT COL?",L:0→dim(L₆
For(I,1,N)
[D](I,L)→L₆(I)
End:Goto 9
Lbl 8:ClrHome
For(I,1,N):I→L₆(I):End
Goto 9
Lbl 6:ClrHome
For(I,1,N):ʟYHAT(I)→L₆(I):End
Lbl 9:ExprOff
Plot3(Scatter,L₆,L₄,▫):ZoomStat:Trace:ExprOn
Goto U
Lbl W
ClrHome:0→R
For(I,1,N)
(ʟRES(I))²+R→R
End:0→T
For(I,1,N-1)
(ʟRFS(I+1)-ʟRES(I))²+T→T:End
T/R→W
Disp "D-W D=",W:Disp "N=",N
Disp "K=",D
Pause :Goto U
Lbl X
ClrHome

{1,N}→dim([A])
Fill(1,[A])
(1/N)*[A]*[D]→[B]:{N,M→dim([E]
For(J,1,M)
For(I,1,N)
[D](I,J)-[B](1,J)→[E](I,J)
End:End
[E]ᵀ[E]→[A]
{M,M}→dim([B])
Fill(0,[B])
Disp "CORR MATRIX":For(I,1,M)
(1/√([A](I,I)))→[B](I,I):End
round([B]*[A]*[B],3)→[C]
Pause [C]
ClrHome:Goto Y
Lbl Z
If Z=0:Goto Y
ClrHome
Disp "UNDER STAT EDIT":Disp "Y IN ʟYVAL,THEN"
Disp "ʟYHAT,ʟRES,ʟSRES":Disp "ʟLEVER,ʟCOOKD"
Disp "FOR LEVERAGE AND":Disp "COOK DISTANCE"
Lbl Y
Return
```

Program FORECAST.83p

```
FnOff :ClrHome
PlotsOff :PlotsOn 3:0→Yscl
Disp "T*S*I MODEL.":Disp
"TIME(1,2,3..N)":Disp "IN L1, Y IN L2-":Disp
"MUST HAVE QRT OR":Disp "MONTH DATA FOR":Disp
"COMPLETE YEARS.":Disp "USES [E].":Pause
ClrHome
Menu("CONT OR QUIT","CONTINUE",A,"QUIT",B)
Lbl B
ClrHome:Stop
Lbl A
ClrDraw:Plot3(xyLine,L1,L2,·):ZoomStat:Trace
Menu("4 OR 12 TERM MA.","4TERM MOVING
A",1,"12TERM M AVERAGE",3,"QUIT",5):Lbl
5:ClrHome:Stop
Lbl 1:4→M
Goto 6
Lbl 3:12→M
Lbl 6
dim(L2→N:N+M→R
R+.5→Xmax
{R,8}→dim([E]
Fill(ε-8,[E])
For(I,1,N)
L1(I)→[E](I,1)
L2(I)→[E](I,2)
End
For(I,N+1,R)
I→[E](I,1):End
M/2+1→A:N-M/2→B
N-M/2→C
B→dim(L3:B→dim(L4:A→K
For(I,1,B)
[E](K,1)→L3(I)
1+K→K:End
For(I,1,B)
0→T:I→J:J+M-1→E:For(D,J,E)
T+[E](D,2)→T
End
I+1→J:J+M-1→E
For(D,J,E)
T+[E](D,2)→T
End
T/(2M)→L4(I)
End
PlotsOn 2
Plot2(xyLine,L3,L4,·):Trace
A→K
For(I,1,B)
L4(I)→[E](K,3)
K+1→K:End
A→K
For(I,K,C)
[E](I,2)/[E](I,3)→[E](I,4):End
A→K:M→dim(L6:Fill(0,L6)
For(I,1,M)
For(J,K,C,M)
L6(I)+[E](J,4)→L6(I):End
```

```
K+1→K:End
L6/(M-1)→L6
(M/(sum(L6))*L6→L6
For(I,1,M/2)
For(J,1,M-1)
L6(J)→H:L6(J+1)→L6(J):H→L6(J+1):End:End
1→K:For(I,1,R/M):For(J,1,M)
L6(J)→[E](K,5)
1+K→K
End:End
For(I,1,N)
[E](I,2)/[E](I,5)→[E](I,6):End
N→dim(L5)
For(I,1,N):[E](I,6)→L5(I):End
Plot2(xyLine,L1,L5,·):Text(0,36,"DESEASONALIZ
ED"):Trace
Menu("TREND FIT TO DS.","LinReg(a+bx)
",9,"QuadReg ",8,"ExpReg ",7,"QUIT",C)
Lbl C:ClrHome:Stop
Lbl 9:11→F
LinReg(a+bx) L1,L5:"a+b*X"→Y6:Goto Z
Lbl 8:22→F
QuadReg L1,L5:"a*X²+b*X+c"→Y6:Goto Z
Lbl 7:88→F
ExpReg L1,L5
"a*b^X"→Y6
Lbl Z:Trace
If F=11:Then
For(X,1,R)
(a+b*X)→[E](X,7):End:End
If F=22:Then
For(X,1,R)
(a*X²+b*X+c)→[E](X,7):End:End
If F=88:Then
For(X,1,R)
(a*b^X)→[E](X,7):End:End
For(I,N+1,R)
[E](I,7)*[E](I,5)→[E](I,8):End
seq(A,A,1,R,1)→L3
For(I,1,N)
[E](I,2)→L4(I)
End
For(I,N+1,R)
[E](I,8)→L4(I)
End
Plot2(Scatter,L3,L4):ZoomStat:Text(0,42,"TREN
D+FORCAST"):Trace
Disp "SEASONAL INDEXES":Pause round(L6,3)
0→dim(L6:1→J
For(I,N+1,R):[E](I,8)→L6(J):1+J→J:End
Disp "FORECAST":Pause round(L6,5):N→dim(L6
For(I,1,N)
[E](I,5)*[E](I,7)→L6(I):End
L2-L6→L6
sum((L6²)/N→M
Disp "MSE=",M
sum((abs(L6)/N→M:Disp "MAD=",M
Pause
```

```
ClrHome:Output(1,1,"IN [E],T IN
C1,"):Output(2,1,"DATA(Y) IN
C2,":Output(3,1,"MA IN C3,
Y/MA":Output(4,1,"IN C4,SI IN
C5,"):Output(5,1,"Y/SI IN C6,FIT
"):Output(6,1,"C6 N C7,C7*SI-
C8)":Output(7,1," TRACE FOR
TREND"):Output(8,1,"(REGEQ)+FORCAST."):Return
```

EXPLORATIONS

INDEX

confidence intervals (*continued*)

  two-sample means

    dependent samples, 85

    independent samples

      σ known, 83

      σ unknown, 82

    two-sample proportions, 86

contingency tables. *See* two-way table

contrast adjustment, 1

control chart, 26

COOLTEMP program, 49

correlation coefficient, 24, 25, 116

correlation matrix, 120

cumSum((under 2nd [LIST] <OPS>), 19, 52

cumulative relative frequency, 18, 19

—D—

data sets. *See* building; track records; marathon
  times; U.S. Census; population by age and race

DEL key. *See* keys for deleting

deleting a list from memory, 9

diagnostic flag, 24

DIM MISMATCH error, 23

display contrast. *See* contrast adjustment

distributions.

  sample proportions, 58

  See also exponential; Poisson; binomial:
    probability

dot plot, 14, 15

Durbin-Watson statistic, 122

—E—

‑E99, E99, 4

edit

  under STAT, 6

editing a list in a spreadsheet, 6

2nd [EE]. *See* keys for entering a number in
  scientific notation

2nd [ENTRY]. *See* keys for returning previous entry
  to screen

estimating. *See* confidence and predictive intervals

expected values, 105

exponential distribution, 71

exponential fit, 32, 33, 49 (ExpReg under STAT
  [CALC])

exponential smoothing, 126–28

—F—

factorial!, 53

five-number summary, 16, 21

FORECAST program, 129

forecasting, 125–32

2nd [FORMAT]. *See* keys for formatting

frequency tables, 11, 12

—G—

geometcdf((under 2nd [DIST], 67

geometpdf((under 2nd [DIST], 67

geometric distribution, 67

goodness-of-fit test, 101

—H—

Histogram

  relative frequency, 14

Histogram plot ⫟⌶⌶, 11–14

home screen, 2

hypergeometric distribution, 68

hypothesis testing

  goodness-of-fit, 101

  nonparametric, 133–42

  one-sample mean

    σ known, 89

    σ unknown, 92

  one-sample proportion, 93

  one-sample standard deviation, 94

  two-sample means

    dependent samples, 97

    independent samples, 95, 96

  two-sample proportions, 98

  two-sample variance (standard deviation), 99

  two-tail test, 90

—I—

2nd [INS], insert mode, 5, 7, 8

interquartile range, 16

invNorm((under 2nd [DISTR], 57

—V—

variability (measures of), 16
variance, 16, 17
1-Var Stats (under STAT <CALC>), 21

—W—

Wilcoxon (Mann-Whitney) test with two
  independent samples, 137
Wilcoxon test with two dependent samples, 135
WINDOW key, 14
WINDOW RANGE Error, 23

—X—

Xscl and Histograms, 12
xyLine plot ⌁, 11, 20, 25, 26

—Y—

Y= key, 2

—Z—

ZInterval (one-sample z confidence interval under
  STAT <TESTS>), 83
ZoomStat (under ZOOM), 12
Z-Test (one-sample z test under STAT <TESTS>), 90